SEEDS OF CHANGE FOR THE AQUARIAN AGE

TRANSFORM

91 Transformational Kriyas & Meditations

VOLUME ONE
MASTERING THE SELF

Kundalini Yoga as taught by Yogi Bhajan®

Kundalini Research Institute
Training • Publishing • Research • Resources

© 2010 Kundalini Research Institute
Published by the Kundalini Research Institute
PO Box 1819, Santa Cruz, NM 87567
www.kundaliniresearchinstitute.org

ISBN 978-1-934532-38-6

EDITOR
Sat Purkh Kaur Khalsa

CONSULTING EDITORS
Nirvair Singh Khalsa, Tarn Taran Singh Khalsa, Gurucharan Singh Khalsa, Guru Raj Kaur Khalsa

CONTRIBUTORS
Tarn Taran Singh Khalsa and Sat Purkh Kaur Khalsa

KRI REVIEW
Siri Neel Kaur Khalsa

COVER DESIGN
Ravitej Singh Khalsa

BOOK DESIGN & LAYOUT
Guru Raj Kaur Khalsa

PHOTOGRAPHY
Grasshopper Photo, Grace Hopper, photographer; Ravi Tej Singh Khalsa, Dev Dharam Kaur,
Gurudarshan Kaur Khalsa, and Sadhu Kaur Khalsa
Cover Photo of Yogi Bhajan's Mala: Narayan Singh Khalsa

MODELS
Adesh Kaur, Ardas Kaur Khalsa, Bhajan Kaur, Bir Kaur O'Flaherty, Deva Kaur Khalsa, Dyal Singh Khalsa, Guru Prakash Singh Khalsa, Har Pal Singh Khalsa, Hargobind Singh Khalsa, Hari Bhajan Kaur Khalsa, Hari Rai Kaur Khalsa, Japa Kaur Khalsa, Jiwan Joti Kaur Khalsa, Jiwan Mukta Singh, Kirn Kaur Khalsa, Lakhmi Chand Singh Khalsa, Nirinjan Kaur Khalsa, Nirmal Singh Khalsa, Panch Nishan Kaur Khalsa, Pritham Kaur (Amelia Becker), Sadhu Kaur Khalsa, Sat Atma Kaur Khalsa, Sat Purkh Kaur Khalsa, Siri Amrit Singh Khalsa, Siri Chand Singh Khalsa, Siri Dyal Kaur Khalsa, Siri Om Kaur Khalsa, Sopurkh Singh Khalsa, Suraj Kaur, Tej Kaur Gaytan, Vanessa Khalsa

Dedication

Photo by Darshan Kaur Khalsa

To our Teacher, the Master of Kundalini Yoga, Yogi Bhajan,
who sacrificed so much to deliver these teachings,
that we might lead, heal and serve the Aquarian Age
with tranquility, transparency, grace and peace.

As another great teacher once said:
"Be the change you wish to see."
Transform your Self and
Transform your world.

Disclaimer

The information contained in this manual comes from ancient yogic traditions. Nothing in this manual should be construed as medical advice. Any recipes mentioned herein may contain potent herbs, botanicals and naturally occurring ingredients which have traditionally been used to support the structure and function of the human body. Always check with your personal physician or licensed health care practitioner before making any significant modification in your diet or lifestyle, to insure that the ingredients or lifestyle changes are appropriate for your personal health condition and consistent with any medication you may be taking.

The Fires of Transformation

FOREWORD FROM THE EDITOR

"The purpose of Kundalini Yoga is transformation." –Yogi Bhajan

At different points in our lives, all of us go through the proverbial fires of transformation. For some it's a break-up, for others it's the death of a loved one, and still for others it's the loss of a job, or a personal health issue, or struggles with addiction. Whatever the fire may be called, we all have to walk through it in order to get to the other side. This process is called transformation and it is, by nature, purifying. It used to be known as alchemy, that mysterious process in which the gross was transmuted into gold. Today we call it consciousness and like the alchemy of old, our personal transformation requires heat, pressure, and time—the purifying fires of *tapas*, the pressure of a sadh sangat, and the discipline of a practice over time—and a little touch of magic I call grace.

Whether it's the psychic heat we create when we burn our egos up with devotion or the physical heat we create when we do Breath of Fire for 31 minutes, each action, though radically different in its outward form, creates *tapas*—or heat—and purifies us, transforms us. Carbon doesn't become a diamond without the tremendous pressure of gravity. As Kundalini Yogis, our gravity is our lifestyle, the practices of this path. It's not easy going out into the world wearing white or covering our head. It isn't easy to change everything—what we eat, what we drink, what time we go to bed—but that is what's required. So, we live in a community of like-minded practitioners—sadh sangat—so that our new way of life is supported and so it's just that much more difficult to veer from the path. We ask for this pressure because it is this pressure that purifies us, purifies our minds and our hearts, bending the curve of self-will toward the will of the Divine, toward devotion.

We've all experienced the transformative power of time, the great healer. Things that seem impossible today are the source of great laughter in the future, and what we do today can change our tomorrow. And, whether we believe it or not, what we do tomorrow can change yesterday. We can transform our stories, those things that defined us in the past and rewrite our destiny. This is the essential element of transformation—that we, ourselves, can be the agents of change within our own lives.

Kundalini Yoga inspired me to change everything. In fact, recently a friend was visiting and she said something that moved me in a way I hadn't anticipated. She said, "You are the most changed person I've ever known." It's taken all the elements, all these seeds of transformation, in order to affect this change in me: the fires of loss and the *tapas* of discipline; the pressure of community and the willingness to dress the part, even when I didn't feel like it; and time—lots of time. Nothing has happened overnight, except perhaps the gift of grace, the strength to say yes, and the willingness to agree to agree, to decide—and along with that decision came the opportunity to begin again.

We hope this newest collection of kriyas and meditations inspires you to begin your own personal transformation today! Practice something new or master something familiar with *Transformation: Seeds of Change for the Aquarian Age*, a two-volume series that brings the tools and technologies of Level Two Teacher Training to your fingertips.

The 91 kriyas and meditations in *Volume One: Mastering the Self* are drawn from across the entire Transformation: Level Two Teacher Training curriculum. Organized to facilitate your personal practice and deepen your experience of the Self, *Mastering the Self* also helps you develop workshops, plan 6-week thematic courses, or assign individual sadhanas with ease. Using each chapter, individually, or combining topics gives you limitless possibilities.

Transformation is the key to success in the Aquarian Age. We hope this becomes just one of the many tools you keep by your side as you change and grow to meet the needs of the times.

Sat Purkh Kaur Khalsa
Editor & Creative Director
Kundalini Research Institute

TRANSFORMATION

INTRODUCTION

There is only one thing in life which is constant—change. Life, by definition, is animated and animation means movement. So if something is alive, it must continually change and transform—it must move. It is not a question of if we want to change or not, but where that change will take us. Where is this journey leading us?

If you practice Kundalini Yoga as taught by Yogi Bhajan®, chances are, at some point you saw the direction your life was taking and decided: "Hey, wait a minute, that's not where I wanted to go!" In that moment of awareness you decided to step off the endless, grinding wheel of karma, and begin your journey down the path of self-awareness.

Yogi Bhajan predicted that as the planet moves from the Piscean to the Aquarian Age, we would witness increasing internal and external turmoil, as old institutions collapsed and the human being became increasingly sensitive. He believed the ancient science of Kundalini Yoga would prove a remarkable technology to balance the glands, strengthen the nerves and help control the mind. But more than that, he believed it would deliver an experience of the Self that would help us not only survive, but also thrive in the coming Age.

I am blessed to have a job that takes me around the world. In my travels I am continually amazed by the technology of Kundalini Yoga, its boundlessness, unfettered by culture, race or society. I also get to witness Yogi Bhajan's predictions about this coming Age coming into being: the institutions of family, church, culture and society, which used to define us, and the course of our lives, are all breaking down and losing their influence on us. These institutions once told us who we were, who we could marry, what professions we could follow, how many children we could have. They defined our beliefs and values. They told us what was right and what was wrong, who was good and who was bad. As these outside institutions lose their control over our lives, two things can happen: we can experience a liberating sense of freedom or we can experience confusion and fear, overwhelmed by the unlimited choices and self-responsibility which confronts us.

Kundalini Yoga is the Yoga of Awareness. The perfect technology for these turbulent, uncertain times, its kriyas and meditations make us sensitive and aware of all our human facets. The sense of awareness opens us up to observe the myriad sensations, thoughts, feelings and desires of the little self, the ego, which constantly whirl through us. With this awareness, we begin to realize the impact they have on the direction of our lives, which takes us deeper, giving us an experience of the True Self whose clarity, calmness and peace are untouched by emotion and commotion. We begin to gain a deep understanding of our humanness and create a relationship between the projections of our ego and our True Self. On a very deep level, the Neutral Mind provides us with a profound experience of Self, so that we can release the pain and anger of the past, face the fear of the future, free ourselves from the chains of our karmic fate and connect ourselves with our spiritual destiny. In doing so, we redefine our identity in relation to our Soul, reestablish our beliefs on a foundation of experience and recreate our habits based on our values, which reflect our deepest Truth.

Through the experience of Self, we come to realize that for the past two thousand years we have had a distorted understanding of human nature. We are not human beings who've come here for a spiritual experience, but rather spirit, come into this life for a human experience. We are not sinful by nature. We are not separated from Heaven. Instead, we are souls whose essence is pure and whose nature is divine. The purpose of life's journey is to uncover that divine essence and experience *cherdi kala*, the ever-rising spirit that brings the peace and happiness of Heaven down to Earth.

"When you are not true to your body, and you have no relationship with your mind and you are not giving rest to your spirit, why would you think that everything should be all right? Forget about great spirituality and all those stories you might have heard: flying at night and descending from the Heavens. That is not the Age of Aquarius. The Age of Aquarius is the knowledge of the Self—willingly learning about the Self and being as devoted as you can be. Asking for yourself, "I am the grace of God, I am the creation of God"; knowing "If you cannot see God in all, you cannot see God at all"; understanding "Live to love and love to live." And when you love, doesn't matter how much time and space tests you, question not, you will win. Question, you lose." –Yogi Bhajan, March 27, 1997

This understanding reflects itself in the simple working principle of Kundalini Yoga: *Sat Nam, Wahe Guru.* Uncover your True Self, *Sat Nam,* connect with your divine essence and, in that moment, you will experience *Wahe Guru,* the pure joy and ecstasy of Being. Your destiny will open up to you and you will finally know true fulfillment.

Transformation: Seeds of Change for the Aquarian Age reflects this basic working principle. In *Volume One: Mastering the Self,* we have organized the Kundalini Yoga Kriyas and Meditations in thematic chapters to guide you on an inward journey toward self-discovery—*Sat Nam.* These tools can help you unlock your inner vitality and give you the strength to face your fear of change; observe, with clarity and neutrality, your habits and your mind's interactions with others; allow you to drop the pain of the past and channel the destructive force of anger into positive, personal transformation; clear and balance your chakras; recognize your own majesty and radiance; and create a deep and fulfilling relationship with your True Self.

In *Volume Two: Serving the Infinite,* the tools to express that joy of experiencing the Self, *Wahe Guru,* and share it with the world around you—opening your heart, sharing your love, using your intuition, and listening deeply—so that you can serve the Infinite creation of the One who created you.

Tarn Taran Singh Khalsa
Director of the Aquarian Trainer Academy
Kundalini Research Institute
January 2010

CONTENTS

Before You Begin

Transformation: Mastering the Self is intended for anyone currently practicing Kundalini Yoga as taught by Yogi Bhajan®. The Kriyas and Meditations included in this manual, however, are considered intermediate level. Some experience is not only recommended but assumed.

Beginning Your Practice—Tuning-In

The practice of Kundalini Yoga as taught by Yogi Bhajan® always begins by tuning-in. This simple practice aligns your mind, your spirit and your body to become alert and assert your will so that your practice will fulfill its intention. It's a simple bowing to your Higher Self and an alignment with the teacher within. The mantra is simple but it links you to a Golden Chain of teachers, an entire body of consciousness that guides and protects your practice: *Ong Namo Guru Dev Namo*. I bow to the Infinite, I bow to the Teacher within.

Ong   Na-mo   Gu- roo   Dayv   Na- mo

How to End

Another tradition within Kundalini Yoga as taught by Yogi Bhajan® is a simple blessing known as The Long Time Sun Shine song. Sung or simply recited at the end of your practice, it allows you to dedicate your practice to all those who've preserved and delivered these teachings so that you might have the experience of your Self. It is a simple prayer to bless yourself and others. It completes the practice and allows your entire discipline to become a prayer, in service to the good of all.

    May the long time sun shine upon you

    All love surround you

    And the pure light within you

    Guide your way on.

    Sat Nam.

Other Tips for a Successful Experience

Prepare for your practice by lining up all the elements that will elevate your experience: natural fiber clothing and head covering (cotton or linen), preferably white to increase your auric body; natural fiber mat, either cotton or wool; traditionally a sheep skin or other animal skin is used. If you have to use a rubber or petroleum-based mat, cover the surface with a cotton or wool blanket to protect and support your electromagnetic field. Clean air and fresh water also helps support your practice.

Practice in Community

Kundalini Yoga cultivates group consciousness, because group consciousness is the first step toward universal consciousness, which is the goal: transcend the ego and merge with Infinity. Therefore, find a teacher in your area. Studying the science of Kundalini Yoga with a KRI certified teacher will enhance your experience and deepen your understanding of kriya, mantra, breath and posture. If there isn't a teacher in your area, consider becoming a teacher yourself. *See our resources page for more information.*

Find a group to practice sadhana (daily spiritual routine) with, or establish a group sadhana yourself—in your home or community center. The Aquarian Sadhana was given by Yogi Bhajan to ground our practice now and into the Aquarian Age. Practicing with others increases the effects of sadhana exponentially. You heal others and others, in turn, heal you. (See *Kundalini Yoga Sadhana Guidelines*, 2nd Edition, available from the Kundalini Research Institute, for more information about creating your own sadhana and guidelines for practicing the Aquarian Sadhana.)

Come together as men and women and share your strength, ask for help when you need it, and laugh together as you participate in this game of life as you heal your Self, serve your community and lead throughout the Aquarian Age

Pronunciation Guide

This simple guide to the vowel sounds in transliteration is for your convenience. More commonly used words are often spelled traditionally, for example, *Sat Nam, Wahe Guru,* or pranayam, even though you'll often see them written *Sat Naam, Whaa-hay Guroo,* and praanayaam, in order to clarify the pronunciation, especially in mantras. Gurbani is a very sophisticated sound system, and there are many other guidelines regarding consonant sounds and other rules of the language that are best conveyed through a direct student-teacher relationship. Further guidelines regarding pronunciation are available at www.kundaliniresearchinstitute.org.

a	hut
aa	mom
u	put, soot
oo	pool
i	fin
ee	feet
ai	let
ay	hay, rain
r	flick tongue on upper palate

CHAPTER ONE

IDENTITY & THE SELF

MASTERING THE SELF

Aligning with the Infinite

There is one question we must all ask ourselves. And that one question is the most important question we will ever ask, because the answer will determine the quality and direction of our life. It will determine whether our life is filled with happiness or sadness, prosperity or poverty, courage or cowardice. Whether we face life's challenges head-on or avoid them in fear; experience fulfillment or frustration; struggle through life with dis-ease or flow through life in health and harmony is largely determined by our answer to this one simple question: Who am I? The answer to that question will determine whether we get caught up—and ground up—by the wheel of Karma, or break free and soar on the wings of Destiny. Although it's a very simple question, the answer is so profound that it will determine the very nature of the Universe and our relationship to it. It will create the reality of our life.

If your answer is "I don't know," then you don't have a clear sense of your identity, and the mind has nothing to orient itself to, which creates insecurity and turmoil. First you must understand that the mind has no fundamental reality of its own. Think of all those thoughts, cascading through your mind, every moment of every day. Think of all the feelings they trigger and all the desires that arise. If your mind has no identity, no central place from which to choose and direct these thoughts, feelings and desires, it jumps all over the place. Your identity provides the framework in which to orient the mind and process your thoughts and feelings.

Second, we must understand that a thought is just an impulse and a feeling is just a sensation, until you identify with it. If we have no identity of our own, then we live in the realm of fantasy and magical thinking and can only process these thought waves through our subconscious doubts and fears, hopes and dreams. Instead of being led toward our destiny, we are pulled in multiple directions; our actions disconnected from the realities of life, on any level. The extremes of this mental state are identified as sociopaths, narcissists and schizophrenics.

If your answer is "I am me," then you have identified with your ego. Although it will provide some grounding and direction to your life, it will ultimately limit you. The ego is a mental faculty, which gives us the illusion that we are separate and unique; it's a survival mechanism of the psyche. Though necessary, we forget it is just that, a mechanism, and we let it become our identity. We become trapped in its small world and see only as far as its limited horizon of time and space, that is, our own lifetime. We become a slave to its futile attempts to control everything and its doomed attempts to hold fast to things which, by their very nature, are transitory.

If your answer is "I am Thine," then you have identified your Self, your reality, as your True Identity: the soul that comes from God and goes back to God. The Soul is part of the Infinite, wrapped up in this human experience, this finite, material realm; yet its home is Infinity. The soul is unborn and undying; knows no fear or anger; is eternally calm and at peace. The soul's only desire is to merge back with the One from which it comes. If this is your identity, then you align your mind with your Destiny. The thoughts and feeling you choose to identify with are not always the easy ones or the pretty ones; they may not bring you worldly wealth and fame, or even material comfort, but they will bring you a deep sense of fulfillment and gratitude.

The person you thought you were when you took your first Kundalini Yoga class and the person you think you are now are two different people. Because, in the end, your personal sense of identity is a mixture of all the facets of human existence, including the two big ones, ego and soul. As you practice Kundalini Yoga you will find that your soul becomes a larger and larger component within that mix, which makes up You. The control your ego once exerted becomes less and less. Ego and soul take you on parallel journeys. Your karma doesn't change; for your karma is your karma. Life will present the same challenges, but how you meet those challenges can take you in completely different directions, two parallel paths. An ego-dominated iden-tity traps you in your karmic wheel of fate. Life grinds you down as you succumb to its challenges by con-tinually reacting with your subconscious agendas and self-destructive habit patterns. A soul-oriented identity will face the same challenges but with the understand-ing that every challenge is an opportunity to grow and expand and uplift ourselves and those around us toward our destiny. Yogi Bhajan often said, "It's not the life that matters, it's the courage you bring to it." Destiny is your Identity in alignment with Infinity; it is an upward mov-ing spiral, which brings a deep sense of fulfillment, hap-piness and peace, also known as *cherdi kala*.

Kriya to Experience Your Own Strength

1. **Bow Pose**. Rock back and forth in Bow Pose, while rhythmically and musically chanting for **6 minutes**.

Har, Har, Har, Har Gobinday	*Creative Infinity Sustains.*
Har, Har, Har, Har Mukanday	*Creative Infinity Liberates.*
Har, Har, Har, Har Udaaray	*Creative Infinity Enlightens.*
Har, Har, Har, Har Apaaray	*Creative Infinity is Infinite.*
Har, Har, Har, Har Hareeang	*Creative Infinity Destoys.*
Har, Har, Har, Har Kareeang	*Creative Infinity Creates.*
Har, Har, Har, Har Nirnaamay	*Creative Infinity is Nameless.*
Har, Har, Har, Har Akaamay	*Creative Infinity is Desireless.*

2. **Pelvic Lifts**. Lie on the back, bend the knees and grab the ankles. Keeping your feet flat on the ground, raise and lower the pelvis. Chant *Har* as you lift up and chant *Har* as you lie back on the ground. Move rapidly. **2 minutes**.

3. Raise the arms over the head but do not let the hands touch. Revolve the upper body counter-clockwise from the base of the spine. Close the eyes and move as if you are in ecstacy. Chant along with a *Ardas Bhaee* recording. **4 minutes**.

4. Stand up with hands overhead, but not clasped. With the eyes closed, dance to *Ardas Bhaee*. **1 1/2 minutes**. Continue dancing. Each time you hear *Sachee Sahee* bend forward, touch the ground, and rise up again to dance. **2 minutes**.

5. Run in place as fast as you can. Move your arms. **2 1/2 minutes.**

6. Repeat exercise 1 for **2 1/2 minutes**.

7. Repeat exercise 2 for **30 seconds**.

8. **Sufi Grind**. Sit up in Easy Pose with hands on the knees. Revolve the torso counter-clockwise. **30 seconds**.

9. Get into **Baby Pose** and sleep. **7 minutes**.

Becoming Crystal Clear

1. Bring the arms straight out to the sides, parallel to the ground, with the palms facing forward. Begin alternately bringing the palms in as if to beat your chest, but do not touch your chest. Breath of Fire will automatically develop from the motion if you do it correctly and powerfully. Imagine that you are pulling pranic energy in with each motion of your hands. **6 1/2 minutes**.

2. Bring the hands forcefully in as if to clap them in front of your face, but do not touch the hands together. Combine force and control in your movement. **2 1/2 minutes**.

3. Move both hands up and down at the same time as if bouncing a ball with each hand. You are bouncing energy against the ground. Breath of Fire. **30 seconds**.

4. Lie down flat and put both hands against the Navel Point and press it hard. Raise the heels up 6 inches and hold. Think you are divine or feel sexy, but keep the heels 6 inches off the ground. **6 1/2 minutes**.

5. Lie down and go to sleep. Imagine that your body is filled with light. Focus at your Navel Point. Listen to *Naad, the Blessing* by Sangeet Kaur. After **8 minutes** begin to sing along using the power of the navel for another **7 minutes**.

Relieving Your Elementary Stress

1. Sit in Easy Pose. Begin clapping the hands in the following sequence:
   a) Slap the thighs
   b) Clap the hands in front of the chest
   c) Open the hands in a V
   d) Clap the hands in front of the chest again
   e) Slap the thighs

Repeat the cycle. (As you repeat the cycle, you will slap the thighs twice in a row.) Create a rhythm. **3 minutes.**

TO END: Inhale deeply and hold the breath for **15 seconds**. Close the eyes and have no thought. Exhale. Repeat holding the breath for **10 seconds**. Inhale and hold for **10 seconds**, inhale more and hold for another **10 seconds**. Exhale.

You will be stress free in exactly three minutes. There is nothing you have to do. One, two, three, four, five. One, two, three, four, five. That's it; it's musical. Your body will start releasing the elementary stress.

2. Begin clapping again in the same sequence and rhythm as Exercise 1. **1 minute.**
TO END: Inhale deeply and hold for 10 seconds. Exhale and relax.

3. Clasp the hands in front of the Heart Center. Fingers of each hand are together and thumbs crossed over each other. Bounce the elbows against the sides of the ribcage. Strike the ribs hard and fast. **3 minutes.**

To end: Inhale deeply and hold for **10 seconds**. Press ribcage tightly with your elbows. Exhale. Inhale deeply and hold for **10 seconds**, hold and tighten the elbows against the ribcage. Exhale. Inhale deeply, hold up to **30 seconds**. Exhale.

4. Sit with the elbows relaxed, fingers spread wide, and hands in front of the shoulders, palms facing forward. Criss-cross the hands in front of the face, as if you were a child, saying 'No, no.' Create your own rhythm. **2 1/2 minutes.**
TO END: Inhale deeply, hold for **10 seconds**, exhale. Repeat twice more and then shake your hands out.

Relieving Your Elementary Stress

5. In Easy Pose, bring the hands to the ground in front of you, allowing the spine to bend gently. Beat the ground with the hands in time with the music. Close the eyes and move rhythmically. **3 1/2 minutes.** Relax. Let the body move with the rhythm. *Music: Punjabi Drums was played during class.*

6. Immediately begin to dance the body in the seated posture. Play with the rhythm. Dance the shoulders. **7–10 minutes.**
TO END: Inhale deeply, hold and exhale. Repeat twice more.

Get rid of arthritis. You have to move the ribcage to create the calcium-magnesium balance. Let your body change the chemistry, relax itself. Free yourself of tension. Dance it away! Give yourself a chance.

7. Place the hands on the Heart Center, right over left parallel to the ground, one hand resting on the other. Close the eyes and nap while seated as gong is played. **8 1/2 minutes.** Rhythmically sit straight and hypnotically go to sleep.

8. Listen and chant with the mantra *Chattr Chakkr Vartee*. **1 minute.**
If you don't know the mantra, just copy the sounds.

> *Chattr chakkr vartee, chattr chakkr bhugtay*
> *Suyambhav subhang sarab daa sarab jugtay*
> *Dukaalang pranaasee dayaalang saroopay*
> *Sadaa ang sangay abhangang bibhootay*

You are pervading and enjoying in all four directions,
You are self-illumined and united with all.
Destroyer of bad times, embodiment of mercy,
You are ever within us, giver of undestroyable power.
—from Guru Gobind Singh's *Jaap Sahib*

COMMENTS

You have no enemy, no poverty, no disgrace. You have nothing wrong with you. It is the elementary stress that causes a zone of horror in you and you become the victim of it. The idea of religion, of meditation, of higher consciousness—call it anything— is that there should be no discontentment in a person. A stabilized, mentally enlightened person is the one who enjoys the spirit, the life. If you want to say you are not corrupt, you are corrupt just in saying it. It's not only a corruption that you wrong somebody; or take away something from somebody; it is a corruption that God gave you the gift of life and you cannot even feel it. Life is a gift. We waste it on our own inner conflicts. We complain to the whole world and whole world complains to us, but we've got to become our own friends. —YOGI BHAJAN

Experience the Original You

1. Sit in Easy Pose. Interlace the fingers and press the palms away from you. This is called reverse elbow lock. Extend the arms straight out in front of you with no bend in the elbow. Stay steady and do not raise or lower your arms once you are in position. Eyes: Tip of the nose.

Breath: One Minute Breath—inhale for **20 seconds**, hold for **20 seconds**, and exhale for **20 seconds**. Continue with a long, slow, deep breath for **3 minutes**.

If you have problems with your stomach and digestion, your elbows may hurt or become uncomfortable.

2. Maintain the mudra with the eyes at the tip of the nose. Continuously inhale through the nose and exhale through the mouth with the force of Cannon Fire. **3 minutes**.

The strength and depth of your breath is in direct proportion to how deeply you can heal yourself now.

3. Maintain the mudra. Inhale, hold the breath and pump your navel. When you can no longer hold your breath, exhale. Immediately inhale and again pump your navel. Continue at your own breath rhythm, pumping your navel as vigorously as you can. **3 minutes**.

Inhale, hold the breath **15 seconds**, stretch your arms out as far as possible, putting pressure on your joined fingers. Exhale through the mouth — Cannon Breath.

Repeat this sequence two more times.

4. To fully circulate the energy you have created, extend the Jupiter finger straight up and lock down the other three fingers with the thumb. Circle the hands in outward circles as fast as possible. This movement has to be so vigorous that the entire spine moves. **2 1/2 minutes**. Inhale and relax.

COMMENTS

If this set is practiced for 120 days, you'll gain great vitality, personal excellence, and a new concept of what you are. It works on the celestial concept of the third layer of the human mind.

A Pure Flame of Light

Sit straight in Easy Pose. Chest out and chin in. Place the hands in Gyan Mudra on the knees, arms are relaxed with elbows slightly bent; the three fingers are straight.

1. Open the mouth and jaw wide. Inhale and exhale deeply through the mouth. Continue with a powerful breath for **3 1/2 minutes**, then inhale deeply and continue with the next exercise.

2. Close the mouth. Begin breathing long and deep through the nose. Meditate and purify yourself. Turn yourself into a flame of light.
2 minutes.

TO END: Inhale and exhale powerfully 3 times. On the third inhale, stretch up, suspend the breath for **15 seconds**, and shake the spine and the hands vigorously to equalize the energy.

COMMENTS

Relationship is nothing but a totally extended experience of self. Breathing through the mouth will relax you very fast. It is a very vital exercise. Note: When teaching this meditation, Yogi Bhajan stated that it should never be done alone, but only in a class situation with an experienced teacher.

Preventing Mega Information Syndrome

PART ONE
MEDITATION FOR CREATIVE IMAGERY

Hands on the knees; eyes closed. Bring the Saturn, Sun and Mercury fingers down onto the pad of the hand. Fingers are straight, not curled. Jupiter finger is pointing away from you and the thumb is pulled back comfortably.

Chant in a monotone: "*I am Gyani.*" (One who is wise.)
Try to sound mechanical, like a computer.

5 minutes

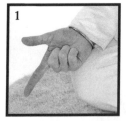

PART TWO
MEDITATION TO PREVENT GOING BERSERK

Christ Mudra: Sun and Mercury fingers are pressed down by the thumb. The Jupiter and Saturn fingers are straight. Hands are on the knees; eyes closed.

Chant in a monotone: "*I am Dhyani.*" (One who meditates.)

5 minutes

PART THREE
MEDITATION FOR FAITH

Thumb holds the Mercury finger down and the three fingers are straight.

Chant in a monotone: "*I am Imani.*" (The faithful one.)

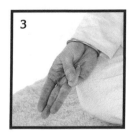

Preventing Mega Information Syndrome

PART FOUR
MEDITATION FOR PENETRATION IN COMMUNICATION

Keep the hands in the mudra from Part 3 but bring the three fingertips together in front of the body between the Heart Center and the Solar Plexus, fingertips pointing forward.

Chant: **Ham Ham Brahm.** *(We are the indivisible vibration of God.)*

5 minutes

PART FIVE
MEDITATION FOR MAKING DEPRESSION DISAPPEAR

Left hand is palm up; right hand is palm down. The hands make an X; lock the thumbs and breathe long and deep.

11 minutes

TO END THE SERIES:
After finishing this series, get up and sing and dance!

TOTAL TIME: **31 minutes**

Meditation to Bless Yourself

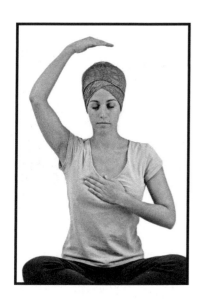

Sit in Easy Pose with an erect spine. Chin in and head balanced.

MUDRA: Place the left palm flat against the heart center. Place the right hand, palm facing down, about 4-6 inches directly above the 10th gate, the crown of the head.

EYES: Closed.

MANTRA: Chant aloud, using the tip of your tongue. Call with grace and reverence, and take your mind into the heavens. Nirinjan Kaur's recording was used.

Ong Namo Guroo Dayv Namo *(I bow to the subtle Divine Teacher within)*

TIME: **11 minutes**. For last **30 seconds**, increase volume and full resonance of the chant. This meditation is best done in the morning.

TO END: Inhale deep, squeeze your body tight. Hold **15 seconds**. Exhale Cannon Fire breath out the mouth. Inhale a second time, squeeze so the energy can go to all parts. Hold **15 seconds**. Cannon Fire out again! Inhale a third time, bring every muscle under your own control, squeeze. Hold **15 seconds**. Exhale Cannon Fire out again. Relax.

COMMENTS

Blessing ourself is a communication with the higher Self in every cell of the body and fiber of our projective aura. It is an act of self-dignity and humility. It accepts that everything is part of the One and that we have a right to bless. Yogi Bhajan says: *"It is the first human right and duty to bless the self and to bless all. It is a function of the spirit as fragrance is the nature of the rose."* To bless, the ego has to be less. Blessings and prayers are closely related. Both require a communication or creation of a common notion. Prayers are the common notion of oneness between you and your Unknown. Blessings are the common notion of elevation and expansion between every finite part of your life and your unlimited self.

What we often neglect is self-blessing. This is not narcissism or a focus to satisfy any need in the ego for recognition. It is more like the responsibility of changing oil in the car or watering the orchids in a greenhouse. When Yogi Bhajan guided the students in this meditation he said:

"As prayer dissolves the gap your mind created between your Self and God, blessing becomes an automatic habit. It is the prerogative of every soul to bless. Sometimes you are taught only to bless others or the less fortunate. Certainly you should bless all, regardless of state and status. To develop it you must also bless yourself. This meditation gives you that experience."

It may be the first time in your life you have learned to bless yourself. Just feel you are blessing yourself, and the sound that you chant calls on the Infinite God. Become very calm, quiet and project your Self into the Heavens. Take your mind to Infinity. Concentrate on the height of your mind. Enjoy the heavens. Feel it is the God within you that repeats this mantra. Just sit in the presence of God and be alert. Direct the mind like a missile to shoot straight up to vastness and Infinity. Drop all limitations. You do everything for everyone—can't you spare 11 minutes for yourself?"

"Blessed are those who bless themselves. Pure are those who purify themselves. Divine are those who worship God in their heart. Graceful are those who give their head in service of others. All the best graces are with those who see God in all for every reason. May this earth and Mother Nature and Heavenly Father be with us as our best friends and may we excel in the new age as people of dignity, divinity and grace. Sat Nam."

Manager Aspect of the Mind

Sit in Easy Pose.

1. Right hand over left, palms face down at heart level. Thumb tips touch and point toward chest. Chant the sound *Har* (the creative energy of Infinity or God) at a steady pace. With each *Har* pull in the navel point and lift the chest up and forward. Then release the navel and allow your lower spine to rock back slightly.

Continue for **3 to 11 minutes**.

2. Put hands in Prayer Pose with the thumbs crossed. Inhale deeply and begin to "chop" with the hands as you chant *Har*. Do it steadily 12 times turning left, then 12 times back to center, then 12 times turning to the right, and finally 12 times back to center. Inhale deeply; begin again.

TIME: **11 to 31 minutes**.

TO END: inhale and hold the breath, press the molars together, and continue the motion for one full cycle. Relax.

COMMENTS

This meditation will integrate your time and how your internal self deals with all the projections through time. It is a core alignment meditation, which defends and preserves the balance of your identity and your projected roles under the pressure of actions, and under the influence of the expectations of others. It actively sets boundaries in relationships. The issue will be insecurity and distrust of appearance of others. It wants to know "What is really going on. What is your intention?" Balanced and fully developed, you can reduce conflicts, uphold the main tasks and mission you took on, and protect your own interests. You are quite capable of delaying pleasure and redirecting impulses in order to reach what is more important to you. It works on the protective Negative Mind and Ahangkar, the ego-sense which claims the impressions of the mind for its own and reacts to them.

Sodarshan Chakra Kriya

Sit in Easy Pose with a straight spine, and a light Neck Lock.

EYES: Eyes are fixed at the tip of the nose.

MUDRA, MANTRA & BREATH PATTERN:
a. Block the right nostril with the right thumb. Inhale slowly and deeply through the left nostril. Suspend the breath. Mentally chant the mantra Wahe Guru 16 times:

Whaa-hay Guroo

Pump the Navel Point 3 times with each repetition, once on **Whaa**; once on **Hay**; and once on **Guroo**, for a total of 48 unbroken pumps.

b. After the 16 repetitions, unblock the right nostril. Place the right index finger (pinkie finger can also be used) to block off the left nostril, and exhale slowly and deeply through the right nostril.

Continue in this pattern.

TIME: **3-31 minutes**. Practitioners may steadily develop this practice to **62 minutes**, to a maximum of **2 1/2 hours** a day.

TO END: Inhale, hold the breath **5-10 seconds**, then exhale. Stretch the arms up and shake every part of your body for **1 minute**, so the energy can spread.

COMMENTS

This is one of the greatest meditations you can practice. It has considerable transformational powers. The personal identity is rebuilt, giving the individual a new perspective on the Self. It retrains the mind. According to the *Tantra Shastras*, it is said to purify your past karma and the subconscious impulses that may block you from fulfilling you. It balances all the 27 facets of life and mental projections, and gives you the pranic power of health and healing. It establishes inner happiness and a state of flow and ecstasy in life. It opens your inner universe to relate, co-create, and complete the external universe.

Treat the practice with reverence and increase your depth, dimension, caliber, and happiness. It gives you a new start against all odds.

"Of all the 20 types of yoga, including Kundalini Yoga, this is the highest kriya. This meditation cuts through all darkness. It will give you a new start. It is the simplest kriya, but at the same time the hardest. It cuts through all barriers of the neurotic or psychotic inside-nature. When one is in a very bad state, techniques imposed from the outside will not work. The pressure has to be stimulated from within. The tragedy of life is when the subconscious releases garbage into the conscious mind. This kriya invokes the Kundalini to give you the necessary vitality and intuition to combat the negative effects of the subconscious mind.

There is no time, no place, no space, and no condition attached to this mantra. Each garbage point has its own time to clear. If you are going to clean your own garbage, you must estimate and clean it as fast or as slow as you want. Start practicing slowly—the slower the better."

—YOGI BHAJAN

CHAPTER TWO

RIDING THE BREATH

MASTERING THE SELF

The Journey of a Lifetime

With every breath we have an opportunity to change. Each breath is a doorway, or a window, to transformation. Each minute, every moment, a pattern is created in time by which we can measure change. If we allow ourselves to be alive and awake and aware, in the moment, change happens.

"Change is the law of life. It is known as the vibratory self-existence. Each prana that comes, rotates our body and gives us an experience. We see, we hear, we feel through these senses and then it goes out, taking with it an image of our state of consciousness in that moment, and then it's called back. This cycle goes in and out all the time, this is the law of cosmic consciousness.

Now if you want to ever change your consciousness you have to have an image, something to relate to. If you relate to Infinity, you can go to Infinity. If you relate to the finite, you go to the finite. This is for you to decide. Nobody is going to decide this for you."

–Yogi Bhajan, April 26,1973

The breath carries our identity. With every inhalation and every exhalation we have an opportunity to witness who and what we belong to—the Infinite. The breath is a gift, just as life is a gift; so with every breath, our identity in Divinity is confirmed and affirmed. The flow of the breath is the flow of the Infinite. The more we identify with that flow, merge in that steady stream, and expand in that consciousness, the greater chance we have for transformation. The greater opportunity we have to release our limited self and expand into our Infinite Self.

Riding the breath means letting go of our rigid notions of identity. It means letting go of our ego and emerging in our Infinite identity. We ride the wave of the breath. We experience ourselves as the inhale and the exhale—*so hang*—*"I am that."* That thing we relate to and call 'I' is simply a wave, a motion; it is momentum. Light is both wave and particle. When we ride the breath, the light of *Sat Nam*, our true identity, becomes a wave of consciousness. We ride that wave to the fullest expression of our Self. When we master the breath, we master prana, the life force. We dance with Shakti and we live more fully.

In order to ride the breath, we must merge with the breath. A surfer doesn't pretend to control the wave; instead, she tunes into the wave, its momentum, its swell, its movement, its power. She understands the ocean's infinite nature. There is no illusion of control. There is only the relationship between balance and surrender, mastery and power. In the same way, we must come into a relationship with the breath and its power so that we can master our Self. For many of us, experiencing the breath is all about controlling the breath. In the initial stages of our practice, control is necessary. We work on breath retention, we begin to understand the movement of the diaphragm, we experience stillness. But in the end, we must transcend technique and come to a deep inner knowing, an alignment of the Self with prana, a surrender to your Infinite identity. So that breath retention becomes less about holding the breath and more about suspending your Self in stillness, witnessing the prana expand and continue expanding the more you surrender. The movement of the diaphragm becomes more about a swinging door than about effort or control; it becomes a balance of the inhale and the exhale that continues on indefinitely, infinitely. We practice so that we can become practitioners. We practice technique so that we can transcend technique and ultimately merge—find union—with the breath. This is yoga.

Breath of Fire...

Segmented Breath...

Alternate nostril breathing...

Sipping the breath...

Chanting and the breath...

... are all facets of mastery. Each technique bears different fruits from the same tree—the breath. Vitality, relaxation, balance and power are fruits of the breath. But for those fruits to truly manifest, the body also has to be in balance. The body is the vehicle for the breath. The pelvis, the spine, the diaphragm, the sinuses, even the way we walk effects our breath capacity. Its depth, its quality, its expansiveness all depend on the body. As yogis, the openness of our pelvis, the balance of our gait, the flexibility of our diaphragm, the length of our spines, all affect our capacity to breathe deeply. The quality of our breath depends largely on its depth. How do we reach the full potential and depth of breath? Movement, flexibility and courage. We have to move; we have to create room for the prana; we have to expand and continue expanding. We have to have a flexible spine, and open pelvis, and a responsive diaphragm. And we have to have courage. The stillness required to suspend the breath requires surrender; surrendering requires courage. In the stillness and space between the inhalation and exhalation and exhalation and inhalation, you face death—both literally and figuratively. You face your fear of death—and nothing transforms us more quickly. Facing that penultimate fear with courage, surrender and faith, we emerge more fully alive, more fully awake.

Ride the breath and take the journey of a lifetime.

Warm-up with Breath of Fire

1. Sit in Easy Pose, hands in Gyan Mudra. Begin Breath of Fire. **3 minutes.**

2. Still in Easy Pose. Extend both arms straight out to the sides horizontally, with the palms up. Begin Breath of Fire. **3 minutes.**

3. Stay in Easy Pose. Have the palms together in Prayer Pose at the Heart Center. Begin Breath of Fire. **3 minutes.**

TO END: Inhale deeply and exhale. Repeat 2 more times. Relax.

Kriya to Prevent Disease

Sit in Easy Pose.

1. Block off right nostril with right Jupiter (index) finger.
Begin inhaling in 4 equal parts mentally chanting:

Saa Taa Naa Maa

Chant while counting off on:
Jupiter (index), Saturn (middle), Sun (ring) and Mercury (little) fingers on
the left hand, with the wrist on the knee (as in Kirtan Kriya).

Then exhale mentally chanting:

Whaa-hay Guroo

in one part with the left hand open. This expands the breath.

TIME: Continue this breathing cycle for **31 minutes** on the left nostril,
then inhale and switch sides:

2. Closing off the left nostril, inhale in 4 equal parts mentally chanting:

Saa Taa Naa Maa

Chant while counting off on:
Jupiter (index), Saturn (middle), Sun (ring) and Mercury (little) fingers on the right hand, with the wrist on the knee.

Then exhale mentally chanting:

Whaa-hay Guroo

in one part with the right hand open.

TIME: Continue this breathing cycle for **31 minutes** on the right nostril.

3. Then switch again back to exercise 1, breathing through the left nostril, same breathing
pattern as before, for 1 more minute to balance it out.

TO END: Inhale, hold, exhale and relax.

Total time for entire kriya: **63 minutes**

COMMENTS
Do this daily for 40 days. It is
good for any chronic illness.

Breathing Through Both Nostrils

1. Sit in Easy Pose with a straight spine, chin in, chest lifted. Lock the Sun fingers down with the thumbs and keep the other three fingers straight. Inhale through both nostrils, pressuring both Ida and Pingala. Inhale with force so that both nostrils squeeze almost shut with the power of the inhalation. As you inhale, bring the hands toward the face as if the strength of the inhalation was pulling them in. On the exhalation, lower the hands back down. Keep your eyes open and look straight ahead, your line of vision parallel to the ground. **3-4 minutes**.

Sometimes you get a headache, breathe through both nostrils three times. See what happens to the headache. It is very powerful.

2. Extend the arms out to the sides, elbows are bent but forearms start out parallel to the floor, palms down. Inhale powerfully through both nostrils in 4 to 6 strokes and shake your hands with each stroke of the breath. Hands are just balanced and the shaking is coordinated with the breath. Practice with power. **3 minutes**.

Your brain will start working right. A lot of oxygen will go right to the brain. These exercises can only be practiced for a very short time, so they must be done with intensity in order to make them work.

3. Close your eyes. Fold the hands in Prayer Pose and place the mudra so that the thumbs are at the tip of your nose. Try to see your hands through your closed eyes. Breathe long, slow, and deep. Make it a healing breath. Pull in prana. **4 minutes**.

TO END: Inhale deeply and exhale deeply and hold the breath out for 10 Seconds. Repeat this breath sequence two more times. Then relax.

Breathing Through Both Nostrils

COMMENTS

If you have done even one breath right, you will have a very good view of your hands through your 'inner eye'. This exercise, which I am developing with you now, will give you a power to see through the walls and see to the Unseen. That's called Agia Chakra.

Concentrate. Concentrate, you can enjoy it, it can give you all that you need. Get lost. These are your powers, which are with you. They are useful things. They are your decorations. They bring you prosperity, they bring you opportunities, they bring you goodwill, they bring you love, they bring you success. These are the things (that work), not telephone calls. The Mastermind must do it for you. Your shaking hands will not shake the world but your mind can shake the Universe. Mind is the most powerful organ.

The idea is to leave the knowledge, idea is not to judge. The one on whose head the crown will sit is the one who will obey and practice.

This exercise is very valuable for your life. When the moment of death comes, and if you have a habit to breathe through both nostrils, you can get it over with. That's how powerful it is. (Breathing through both nostrils is very neutralizing because it activates the Shushmana naadi.) A neutral person is not punishable by God because neutral breathing becomes Divine. When Ida and Pingala meet, the only existing (channel) is Shushmana. And when Shushmana is active, there is no sin, punishment or authority of anything which can take you to the wrong corner. Can you believe how easy it is? But you have to develop it.

We are working scientifically with the Agia Chakra (6th chakra) to develop the frontal lobe and the hypothalamus. The hypothalamus controls your automatic functions and the frontal lobe controls your personality. If these two areas are not developed, it will create a situation that will downgrade your life, doesn't matter what else is working for you.

—YOGI BHAJAN

Meditation to Alleviate Your Stress

Sit in a comfortable meditative posture with a straight spine, chin in, and chest lifted. Hands in Gyan Mudra or any other comfortable meditative mudra.

EYES: Close the eyes and concentrate on the breath.

BREATH: Inhale through the nose in a Segmented Breath with 8 equal strokes. Exhale through the nose in one deep and powerful stroke.

TIME: **11 minutes**

TO END: Inhale deeply and hold the breath 5-10 seconds. Exhale. Inhale deeply and hold the breath 15-20 seconds and roll your shoulders. Exhale powerfully. Inhale deeply and hold the breath 15-20 seconds and roll the shoulders as fast as you can. Exhale and relax.

Meditation on the Flow of Life

1. Sit straight in a cross-legged position. Eyes are closed.

Stretch the left arm straight out to the side, from the shoulder, with the palm down.

Raise the right hand so that the elbow comes away from the body and begin sweeping the lower arm in a circular movement.

On a deep inhalation, through pursed lips, bring the energy in as you move your hand toward your mouth.

Exhale through the nose as you complete the circular motion. Palm is slightly cupped.

Open the chest. Give yourself power.

11 minutes.

2. Place the hands on the heart. Do Long Deep Breathing through the nose. Calm down, relax, go deep.

3 minutes.

TO END: Inhale deeply and hold for 10 seconds. Expand the chest while pressing the heart as hard as you can and lengthening the spine as much as you can. Take the energy all the way up. Cannon Fire Exhale. Repeat twice more. Relax.

Pranic Body Physical Body

1. Sit in Easy Pose with the right elbow bent, forearm angled up, and the right palm facing downward. Concentrate on the right hand. Keep the hand parallel to the floor. Move it to the right. Then back to center. Move it to the left, then back to center. Keep the palm facing downward. **1 minute**.

Sometimes your hand will move in one direction a little bit more or less. The direction or angle may be wrong. You will find that what you want to do is not happening. You will see that there is a difference between the command you send to your hand and its obedience. Observe this situation in this exercise.

2. Bend both elbows with the forearms angled up and both palms facing downward. The upper arms are relaxed by the sides of the body. The hands are together in front of the chest, thumbs near each other but not touching.

Move both Mercury (pinkie) fingers down and up at the same time.
Then move both Sun (ring) fingers down and up at the same time.
Then move both Saturn (middle) fingers down and up at the same time.
Then move both Jupiter (pointer) fingers down and up at the same time.
Continue moving the same fingers of each hand at the same time.

Move only the set of fingers that you are trying to move. Do not move any of the others. **2 1/2 minutes**.

Look at your hands, seriously concentrate, and coordinate the movement. Your efforts will show that you have two brains, not one. Both movements will not be exactly the same, no matter what you do. This is a simple physical fact and is very hard to accept. You should be aware that everything is not under your control. It is not a handicap. It is a reality.

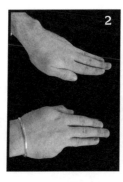
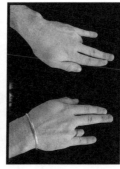
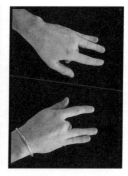
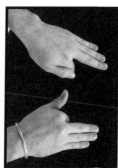

Pranic Body Physical Body

3. Stand up, bend the knees, and lower yourself down as if you were sitting in a chair. Imagine that you are sitting comfortably in a chair. Stay in this position. Keep your back straight and your spine relaxed. **3 minutes**.

I am working with the organs of your body to let you know that because of the nonflexibility and rigidity which you have created, your functional body and your commanding body are not in the same position. I want you to know this because this situation creates a handicap.

4. Sit down on the right heel with the left leg stretched out straight. Grasp the heel of the left foot with both hands and lift the leg up six inches. Lift it six inches only, no higher. Keep the left leg straight. Hold this position for **1 1/2 minutes**.

Remain in this posture, close your eyes, and do Sitali Breath: inhale through the rolled tongue and exhale through the nose. Breathe heavily. **1 1/2 minutes.**

Change legs and continue the exercise sitting on the left heel, with the right leg stretched out in front. Grasp the right heel with both hands and lift the leg up six inches. Begin a powerful Breath of Fire. **2 minutes**.

In your body you have an organ called the colon. It gives you life. It gives you all that your body needs. If you can hold your leg straight and keep it in position for this exercise, you can help to strengthen your colon. This is one of many small cleansing kriyas that we do to affect certain important organs in our bodies.

On the left side we have done a cooling Sitali breath and on the right side we have done a heavy and hot Breath of Fire. Both must be done. Do not do one side and not the other. A couple of minutes of this breathing will trigger in you the strength that you cannot buy or capture.

5. Sit in Easy Pose and bring the soles of the feet together. Lock the hands around the feet, lift the feet off the ground, and balance yourself. It will be an angular balance. Do not let your feet touch the ground. Stick out the tongue as far as you can and begin panting—Dog Breath. Make the breath deep and rhythmic. **1 1/2 minutes**.

This exercise is said to eliminate mucous and to take away sexual weakness.

continued on next page

Pranic Body Physical Body

6. Come into Cobra Pose.

   a) Begin rapidly opening and closing the lips. **1 1/2 minutes**.

     You will get a very funny feeling, but it is alright.

   b) Stay in Cobra Pose and begin wrinkling your nose. Pull your nose upward. **1 minute**. It is very relaxing.

     This exercise can get a tremendous amount of hate out of you. Get rid of it.

   c) Still in Cobra Pose, begin rolling the lower jaw, like a cow chewing its cud. The lower jaw moves around in a circle. **1 minute**.

     This is a very relaxing movement.

7. Sit in Easy Pose and stretch the arms out to the sides. Begin moving your arms up and down like you are flying. Imagine that you are flying a long distance. Close your eyes and concentrate on flying. **11 1/2 minutes**.

Fast or slow, set your own rhythm. Move in any pattern you wish, but whatever rhythm you start with, you have to continue in that rhythm. What we are doing is setting a movement and asking our neuro-message system to copy it. It is very important. You must recapture your original pattern and repeat it. It is all happening inside the brain and the movement of the hands is just a path to create it. It should not hurt.

TO END: Stretch your arms straight to the sides like an eagle gliding. Make your arms and hands like steel. Toughen every muscle in your arms, shoulders, and neck. Stretch and toughen. **1 minute**.

8. Relax.

Awaken the Dormant Power Within

Sit in Easy Pose with a straight spine.

MUDRA
Bend the elbows down into the sides. Extend the forearms straight up, so the hands are in front of each shoulder, the palms facing one another, with about an 18-inch space in between the two hands. The fingers point towards the ceiling. Bend the ring and mercury finger into the palm, and hold them down with the thumb. The index and middle fingers are spread wide to form a V. Make sure you keep these two fingers spread wide the entire time.

MOVEMENT
Extend bent elbows up and out to the sides, so they are parallel to the ground. With a forceful motion, bring elbows down and into the body, to slap against the 7th rib with full force. This movement will cause the shoulders and body to vibrate. Do it in a rhythmic, dancing motion, to the beat of the tape. Let head and shoulders move with the music. Move at a fairly rapid pace, about one time a second.

EYES: Unspecified.

BREATH: Should become Breath of Fire.

MUSIC: Recording by Matamandir Singh: *Gobinday Mukanday* (with English poetry interspersed)

TIME: Done in class for about **23 1/2 minutes**.

TO END: Inhale deeply, stretch your arms up tightly, and lift your body to the extent you stretch your spine. Hold tightly for 15 seconds. Relax.

COMMENTS
The sound of the breath must touch the Heavens and it must be hot. It will become like Breath of Fire. You must awaken the dormant power within you and penetrate all the cycles of transmission of your magnetic field energy, which governs your essence to become a greater exalted person, to face everything with grace. That's the beauty.

Maha Gyan Agni Pranayam

Sit in a comfortable meditative posture, with the spine straight, chin in and chest out.

MUDRA: Cup the hands at heart level with the fingertips touching. The hands make a "little boat." Make sure that the outsides of the hands from the Mercury (pinkie) fingers all the way to the base of the palms are touching as much as possible. Place the thumbs just inside the hands and bend them down at the knuckle ninety degrees. The thumbs touch each other and your hands. It is a snug position.

EYES: Closed.

CHANT: Inhale deeply and chant in a monotone, eight times in one breath:

> *Ek Ong Kaar, Sat Gur Prasaad*
> *Sat Gur Prasaad, Ek Ong Kaar*

TIME: Begin by practicing this kriya for **11 minutes** and slowly build up to **31 minutes**.

COMMENTS
This is a very powerful kriya. *Maha Gyan* means "the great knowledge." Agni means the "purity of fire." Practice this kriya unto that Infinity of God.

Mul Mantra for Vitality

Sit in Easy Pose.

MANTRA: Chant the Mul Mantra, **inhaling completely before each line**:

Ek Ong Kaar
Sat Naam
Kartaa Purakh *(let the whole breath go through the nose)*
Nirbho, Nirvair
Akaal Moorat
Ajoonee
Saibhang
Gurprasaad
Jap *(let the whole breath go through the nose)*
Aad Sach *(release breath with a hiss)*
Jugaad Sach *(release breath with a hiss)*
Haibhee Sach *(release breath with a hiss)*
Naanak Hosee Bhee Sach *(release breath with a hiss)*

Each time you inhale, you must do so to your maximum capacity and each phrase must use up the entire breath. On words like *Akaal Moorat*, where the sound isn't really extended, release the breath through the mouth with a light "uhh…" sound.

On *Kartaa Purakh* and *Jap*, release the breath through the nose. This is the whole secret: the last four phrases end with the breath released through the mouth so the "*ch*" sound in *Sach* is like the extended sound of a hissing snake.

TIME: Chant for a minimum of **11 times a day for 40 days**. Since each person has a different lung capacity, this meditation should be done individually instead of in a group.

COMMENTS

To brighten your auric light, have a radiant face and prevent yourself from aging, practice this meditation. This is one of five meditations given specifically "to prepare for the gray period of the planet and to bring mental balance."

CHAPTER THREE

STRENGTHENING
YOUR RADIANCE

MASTERING THE SELF

Be the Light

"When you understand who and what you are, your radiance projects into the universal radiance and everything around you becomes creative and full of opportunity."
                                        –Yogi Bhajan

R adiance is our projection. We affirm who we are through the word—*Sat Nam*. We experience who we are through the breath—*so hang*. We deliver who we are through our radiance—*Wahe Guru*! Yogi Bhajan often said our presence should be a healing. Can you imagine walking into a room and sensing the deep breath, the sigh of relief, your presence brings? Can you imagine your radiance uplifting someone from across a room, someone you've never even met or may never meet? This is what is asked of us in the Aquarian Age. As leaders, teachers, healers, and yogis, our presence is our radiance; and if our presence cannot deliver, nothing will.

"If you are human and your presence doesn't work, all the wealth and all the knowledge will not work either. Once you develop a personal discipline, your psyche starts emitting a sense of confidence, trust, and grace— and that creates love. You radiance should be so strong, that even if a hateful person sees you, it should totally neutralize the other person's psyche so that they experience nothing but love and friendship."
                        –Yogi Bhajan, November 27, 1995

Radiance is our shine—our inner light. It's what attracts opportunity and prosperity into our lives. It's what protects us from fear and hatred. Our Radiant Body is our protection; but it is also our projection, a witness to our royal courage, our grace, and our willingness to be of service to others. As we approach the Aquarian Age, the pressure we are experiencing now will only increase. These days and times demand a strong nervous system, a clear arcline and a radiant aura; these elements, along with a vibrant Pranic Body contribute to the health and strength of our Radiant Body. If our Radiant Body is weak, we become susceptible to paranoia and delusions, and unable to serve others or our own destiny.

We begin by balancing the aura so that it can fully contain and sustain our energy and our projection. Just like a hurricane lantern, the flickering light needs to be contained in order to shine brighter. So too, our inner light needs a strong aura to maintain our projection. We then bring our awareness to wisdom—*gyan*—and see the light of the mind strengthen and sustain our capacity to project and radiate love, kindness and compassion. In the meditation for the Radiant Body, the mantra *Ajai Alai* is used to develop and strengthen the Arcline and the Crown Chakra.

Finally, we work on the Pranic Body with both Shabd Kriya and Charn Jaap. The quality of our breath strengthens the radiance of our projection. Just as air is needed to keep the light aflame, so, too, our bodies and minds need the flow of the breath in order to power our lives, in each moment, and into the future. Be the light and illumine every dark corner of the world.

Kriya for Balancing the Aura

1. Sit in Easy Pose. Bend the elbows out to the sides at shoulder level and slightly cross the hands in front of your open eyes. Spread the fingers wide, like a fan. Then move your upper arms from the elbow, bringing the hands slightly out to the side and back again. The upper arm will be parallel to the floor. Continue this motion rapidly and forcefully for **3 minutes**.

This exercise works on the eyes.

2. Stand up and move into Archer Pose, with the right leg bent forward so the knee is over the toes. The left leg is straight back with the foot flat on the ground at a 45° angle to the front foot. Raise the right arm straight in front, parallel to the ground and make a fist, with thumb pointing up as if grasping a bow. Pull the left arm back as if pulling the bowstring back to the shoulder. Face forward with the eyes fixed on the horizon above the fist. From this position begin bending the right knee so the body drops down, and then comes back up.

    Continue this motion powerfully and rhythmically for **2 minutes**.
    Switch sides and continue for **2 more minutes**.
    Switch sides and continue for **30 seconds** more.

3. Come into Cobra Pose. Lie down on the stomach with the palms flat on the floor under the shoulders and the heels together with the soles of the feet facing up. Arch the spine from the neck to the base until the arms are straight with elbows locked. From this position, raise the buttocks up into Triangle Pose supporting yourself on your palms and soles of your feet, with your body forming straight lines, heels to buttocks and buttocks to wrists. Then return to Cobra Pose. Alternate movements at a speed of 2 seconds per posture for **5 minutes**.

Kriya for Balancing the Aura

4. Sit in Easy Pose with a straight spine and play the recording of the *Wahe Guru Jio* meditation (by Bhai Avtar Singh). When you hear the words *Wahe Guru* or *Wahe Jio*, pull Mulbandh, pulling in on the muscles of the rectum, sex organs and Navel Point for the length of the phrase, then relax and meditate on the words in between. When you hear the **Toohee**, take one powerful Breath of Fire, an equal inhale and exhale from the abdomen for the length of the word, then relax and meditate in between. Continue for at least one cycle of the meditation (approximately **14 minutes**).

This meditation moves the energy from the third chakra out into the aura, and returns to the third chakra energizing each chakra. If you practice it for the full length of the recording for 90 days, you will perfect the meditation.

COMMENTS

This set builds your physical energy and stamina. It strengthens the navel energy. Then it rhythmically moves the meridian energy from the Third Chakra to the Eighth Chakra and back. This dance of energy builds all the chakras and the radiance of the aura. It is the kind of kriya you can master gradually and that becomes increasingly delightful as your aura expands.

Become Aware, Intelligent & Radiant

Sit in Easy Pose with the eyes closed and move smoothly through the series without any break. This is a guided meditation. Yogi Bhajan called it a "therapy."

1. Shake hands with the unknown and visually see the (Jolly) Green Giant as you continue the motion of shaking hands. Watch him carefully. If you are concentrating right, you will not feel easy and normal. If you feel any abnormality, you are fortunate, because you are in it. Continue for **1 to 1 1/2 minutes**.

2. Immediately imagine yourself to be on the top of the Empire State Building and feel you are hugging the biggest ape on the planet. Feel, smell and understand; and just see the relevance of it. Look down from the height and hold, understand your parameter. Tranquilize yourself and hold on strongly. Continue for **1 minute**.

3. Come down and imagine you are in a restaurant holding a knife and fork in two hands and using them to eat. Order your drinks, order your food. Visualize yourself eating and drinking and feel good. Continue for **1 1/2 minutes**.

4. Now you have come back home. Imagine you are standing before a full length mirror naked. Through the "O" of the mouth begin long complete breaths in and breathing out into the mirror through the rounded lips. Suck in the entire prana and then exhale pushing out all the weakness and disease. Concentrate consciously. Each breath should be stronger than the one before. Continue for **3 1/2 minutes**.

5. Continue the same breath. Immediately interlace your fingers and raise them over your head, palms down, forming an Arcline. The hands are 4-6 inches above the head. and open your chest as much as you can. Use your mental strength. Open up your mental pores. Continue for **3 minutes**.

6. Place the right hand over the left on your chest at heart level. Chant the mantra *Har Har Har Dam*, pulling the navel strongly on the sound *Dam*. *Dam* sounds like *hum*. Speak loudly and from the Navel Point. Continue for **5 1/2 minutes**.
To End: Deeply inhale. Suspend the breath **15 seconds** as you press, with both hands, as hard as you can on the chest. Exhale like a cannon firing out through the mouth. Repeat this 2 more times and then on the last repetition as you hold the breath tighten the muscles from the base of the spine all the way to the top. Relax.

COMMENTS

The mantra *Har Har Har Dam* means "every breath of God." *Har Har Har* is for the creative force of the infinite and *Dam* is for navel power and manifestation. Life is prana and it is based on *pavan guru*, that is how life is. This creates the glow of your Radiant Body which is what makes you attractive to others. That is a shining armor around you, for your protection and attraction.

Gyan Chakra Kriya Meditation

Sit in Easy Pose. It is important to sit with a straight spine.

MUDRA: Hands are in Gyan Mudra (the tip of the thumb and the tip of the index finger together). Keep the other three fingers straight and pressed together side by side. Stretch your arms over your head. Create a steady movement: Begin making large alternate circles of the arms. The right arm swoops in a large counterclockwise circle over the head, back behind the body and then out to the right as low as the heart center. The left arm moves in a large clockwise circle over the head, back behind the body and out to the left. Stagger the movement of the two arms. As the left arm comes over the head, the right arm is circling out to the right of the body. As the right arm moves towards the head, the left arm moves out to the left of the body. This way the arms won't collide with one another. Keep the arms circling up and around and move forcefully in rhythm with the mantra, one revolution per second.

MANTRA: Chant clearly and forcefully from the Navel Point to the recording of *Sat Nam Wahe Guru*, Indian Version #2, with this mantra:

Sat Naam, Sat Naam, Whaa-hay Guroo, Whaa-hay Guroo

TIME: Continue for **11 minutes**. For the last **30 seconds**, move as fast as possible.

TO END: Inhale, stretch the arms straight up to hug the ears and stretch the spine as much as possible. Hold **10 seconds**, exhale and repeat two more times. During the last inhale and stretch, twist the body first left then right seven times then come to center and exhale.

COMMENTS

Gyan Chakra Kriya Meditation is one of the most sacred kriyas in Kundalini Yoga. It was practiced so miracles could happen. There is a story associated with it: Over 2,000 years ago Rishi Anand saw with his intuitive eye that a great weather shift and famine would strike the country and create much hardship and death. He asked all the monks in his ashram to practice this every day, selflessly. After three years, the famine struck hard. The monks had attracted opportunity, wealth and prosperity and had stored a lot of food. So they opened free kitchens and distributed their food, and brought more in from great distances. They saved humanity for two full years until the effects of the famine had passed.

This meditation is fantastic for healing. It helps the heart and joints. It lowers stored anger. It increases intuition. In 120 days of steady practice you will change and your capacity to realize change changes. Its primary effect is that it brightens your halo. It builds the Aura. It activates the Arcline, which taps the knowledge from the aura and akasha. That is why the Arcline is called the seal of knowledge. Life becomes different. You realize your reality and much prosperity runs to you. Your radiance and presence communicates and elevates your life. As a personal practice, do it regularly for 120 days.

Meditation to Develop the Radiant Body

Sit straight in a cross-legged position. Arc the arms over the head, with the fingers interlocked in-between the palms. Tuck the chin in, and pull the arms back and slightly downward until the hands are above the back of the neck. With the hands in this position, the fingertips are pointing down and the thumbs extend back behind you.

MANTRA: Sing the *Ik Acharee Chand shabd*:

Ajai Alai Abhai Abai
Abhoo Ajoo Anaas Akaas
Aganj Abhanj Alakh Abhakh
Akaal Dyaal Alaykh Abhaykh
Anaam Akaam Agaahaa Adhaahaa
Anaathay Pramaathay Ajonee Amonee
Na Raagay Na Rangay Na Roopay Na Raykay
Akaramang Abharamang Aganjay Alaykhay

Recording by Gurushabd Singh and Nirinjan Kaur recommended.

TIME: Do the meditation for **11-22 minutes**.

TO END: Inhale deeply, hold the breath and stretch the arms up high keeping the fingers interlaced. Exhale powerfully. Repeat 2 more times. Relax, shake out the hands.

COMMENTS

This extraordinary meditation is to be done with great precision. Make sure the hand mudra and the position of the hands over the head are held correctly and fixed.

As you do the *Ik Acharee Chand* mantra, hear each word as a world—each word as complete as you speak, projecting with the fifth chakra and vibrating the sound as naad with the eighth chakra.

This will build and expand the Radiant Body. It is through this expanded Radiant Body our communication becomes impersonally personal. It is natural to give gratitude to the golden link, to our teacher Yogi Bhajan and to show reverence for the sacred space of the teacher within and without.

When the Radiant Body is weaker, we feel we have to do everything. We're better than some people and worse than others. When our hidden agendas are put aside and our radiance strong, our presence embodies our essence. We are beyond comparison and act in love and duty to all. We take no finite claim. We act in love and dissolve ourself in the rhythms of infinity without hesitation. Without the full Radiant Body we grasp for some security other than our Being and the Infinite. With the Radiant Body strong, our presence communicates contentment, containment, completeness and consciousness.

Meditation for Balance in the Circumvent Force

Sit with the spine straight and draw the left knee up to the chest. Keep the left foot flat on the ground. Hold the knee against the chest with the hands. Place the right ankle over the top of the left foot. Pull the spine perfectly straight.

BREATH: Inhale as the forehead is lowered to the knee. Maintain Neck Lock. Hold the breath. Then exhale and raise the energy into the Third Eye Point as you lift your head. The breath rhythm is:

Inhale and drop the head	**5 seconds**
Hold the head at the knee	**15 seconds**
Exhale and lift the head	**5 seconds**

TIME: Continue **26 times**, then switch legs for 26 more repetitions.

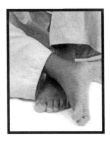

COMMENTS

Suppose with every adversity against you, you want to defend and project yourself in an encounter. Use your *sahasrara*—the Crown Chakra—and use your presence and your aura (the eighth chakra). Remember, you used to have a teacher called Yogi Bhajan. He used to say, "When your presence doesn't work, nothing works anyway!"

Let's do this pranayam to strengthen the circumvent force so we can feel balanced, protected, confident and elevated in our responses.

The most difficult part of the aura to alter is the circumvent force. Whenever the energy flow in and out of the body is imbalanced, a weakness develops in the auric radiance from that area of the body. A slight imbalance can produce a loss of three feet in radiance. "This meditation is a spiritual cure," and brings a balance to your energy flow. It restores and recharges the divine protective shield around you. If this shield is strong, every negative energy that approaches you can be changed to positive in its effect on your consciousness.

Shabd Kriya

Sit in any comfortable posture with the spine straight.

MUDRA: Place the hands on the lap, palms up with the right hand over the left. The thumbs are together and point forward.

EYES: Focus the eyes on the tip of the nose, the eyelids half-closed.

BREATH & MANTRA:
Inhale in 4 equal parts, mentally vibrating the mantra

Saa Taa Naa Maa

Hold the breath, vibrating the mantra 4 times for a total of 16 beats. Exhale in 2 equal strokes, projecting mentally

Whaa-Hay Guroo

TIME: 15 to 62 minutes.

COMMENTS

The best time to practice this Kriya is every night before bed. If it is practiced regularly, sleep will be deep and relaxed and the nerves will regenerate. After a few months, the rhythm of your breath as you sleep will be subconsciously regulated in the same rhythm! You will think better, work better, share better, love better and exercise better. This rhythmic mantra will eventually progress so that even in daily activities you will automatically hear the mantra and take on the breath rhythm.

Mystically, the effect is understood in numerology. The number 11 is the number of Infinity in the material world and it is the conqueror of the physical realm. The number 22 is the infinite number of longing and mastery in the mental realm. The breath is regulated in 22 beats and gives the mind the power to stretch to the Infinite.

There cannot be enough praise of this meditation and its growth-promoting effect on the personality. It gives radiance and that radiance gives patience which is the first condition of real Love. In Love, you give, without attention to all the mistakes of another, as the sun gives light and warmth to all people. Incorporating this universality within the personality comes with the disciplined practice of Shabd Kriya.

Charn Jaap

The following walk can be done by an individual, or by a couple. This is a very sacred meditation done in the following way:

As the left foot hits the ground chant:

Sat Naam

As the right foot hits the ground chant:

Whaa-hay Guru

Walk consciously, 3 miles a day for 90 days.

If practicing as a couple, hold hands. Have your hands moving in the same direction as your legs, like a soldier marching. Be very conscious of moving the arms, the body, and the footwork. Try to walk in unison; breathe in unison as you chant.

COMMENTS

This walk helps you to pick up the electromagnetic field. Many problems can be answered by this walk. It is a recommended meditation for couples who are trying to conceive a child.

CHAPTER FOUR

MASTERING THE TATTVAS & BALANCING THE CHAKRAS

MASTERING THE SELF

Command of the Self

Tattvas represent the five qualities that make up the physical world: earth, water, fire, air and ether. We all have a predominant tattva. Maybe you're fiery, quick to react. Or, maybe you're etheric—not quite 'of this world'. Each tattva reflects its own qualities in our behaviors, habits, and constitution. We observe this all the time. Much like an ayurvedic physician's diagnosis, balancing these tattvas is more complicated than it may seem on the surface. Perhaps we need to increase earth or reduce fire in order to balance the air. Each person has a unique constitution, and therefore, a unique solution. The beauty of Kundalini Yoga as taught by Yogi Bhajan® is that it is a self-correcting, adaptogenic practice. The body adopts what is needed in order to establish balance and harmony.

To master our tattvas, we must first identify our own predominant tattva, the quality that defines us, and begin to practice in a way that brings it into balance. Mastering our tattvas means transcending them, and ultimately, being able to call on them at will. Kirtan Kriya is probably the best practice for bringing our tattvas into balance. It's one of the five kriyas Yogi Bhajan indicated as essential for the Aquarian Age. If all else were lost and we just did Kirtan Kriya, we would make it through the change of the Age with grace, strength and equanimity.

The first act of raising the kundalini is to tie our hair in a rishi knot at the crown of our heads. This simple act draws the solar energy down into the body—and the energy of the body must respond! The kundalini rises to balance the solar energy. It's that simple; it's natural. Being Human: Balancing Heaven & Earth creates that same effect; we consciously generate the balance of Heaven and Earth within the body and within the Self. We're balancing our energy system, our chakras, which represent the many gifts of the self-sensory human. Each of the seven primary chakras delivers a gift—and a challenge. The awakening of the kundalini brings balance to all the chakras and heals us so that we can in turn serve and heal others.

The place where being human begins is where Heaven and Earth meet, at the Heart Center, the Fourth Chakra. This is where we awaken to the Neutral Mind, conscious compassion and true love. We become human, literally, 'the light of the mind' and awaken to group consciousness. We extend ourselves in service, we forgive, and we love, unconditionally. These sound like the qualities of a saint; but they are simply the traits of an awakened human spirit.

As we consider this balance of Heaven and Earth, let's look at the gifts of the upper and lower triangles. The chakras related to the lower triangle include the first, second and third:

The gift of our First Chakra is security. We are grounded, stable, centered and loyal. We have a strong constitution and are accepting of ourselves and others. We embody the Earth element and nurture and support those around us.

The gift of the Second Chakra is creativity. We are relaxed and positive; we flow with life as water flows. We are patient, like the repose of a mountain lake we exude a calm that only comes from deep reflection.

The gift of the Third Chakra is identity. We are courageous and committed with a healthy sense of Self. This is where our strength lies—our fire—the seat of the kundalini. Our strengths and weaknesses of the lower triangle are addressed with the Pelvic Balance Kriya, which provides a solid foundation for the initiation and movement of the kundalini.

Looking at the gifts of Heaven, the upper triangle, we begin at the throat, the Fifth Chakra. The gift of the Fifth Chakra is authenticity. We speak the truth, we live our truth, and we teach the truth. It is here that we align our will with God's will and live to inspire others.

At the Third Eye, the Sixth Chakra, we find the gift of insight and intuition. We understand our purpose and we bring our will and our projection to serve it. This is the seat of the yogi—the union of the opposites.

The gift of the Seventh Chakra is Infinity—no separation. Here, we crown ourselves, experience our vastness and dwell in a state of bliss.

Finally, we come to the aura, our Eighth Chakra, which projects and protects. Technologies for the Eighth Chakra can be found in Chapter Three: Strengthening Your Radiance.

Yogi Bhajan said that you can't 'move' the energy of the chakras, you can only bring them into balance. So our practice is not about manipulating these energies or their gifts, but instead, becoming a thoughtful and present witness to them—when they are out of balance and when they come into balance. It's about awareness. Each kriya seeks to balance all the chakras so that we can more fully embody the self-sensory human, so that we can transform and deliver that transformative experience to others.

"If a man, under any circumstances, makes it his daily routine to do Sat Nam Kriya (Kirtan Kriya) with the navel, that will take care of the five tattvas; and, I tell you very frankly, if you do Sat Kriya for 11 minutes, it will take care of the chakras and keep them open; and if you do this Wahe Guru Kriya (Sodarshan Chakra Kriya) which we have just done, it will give you excellence; and that's how you should meet the Age of Aquarius; with strength, not weakness."

–Yogi Bhajan, December 20, 1996

Warming Up

1. Yoga March. Coordinate the breath with the movement of the arms up and down, and alternate knees up and down. Inhale arms and knee up, exhale arms and knee down. Powerful breath. **3 minutes.**

2. Sitting in Easy Pose grab the ankles, and do Spinal Flex. Inhale arch the spine forward, lift the chest up, exhale back. Keep head level. Powerful breath. **3 minutes.**

Warming Up

3. Torso Twist. Grab the shoulders, and lift elbows up and back, at shoulder height. Inhale twist whole torso and head to the left, exhale to the right. **3 minutes**.

4. Shoulder Shrugs. With hands resting on the knees or thighs, inhale and bring the shoulders up towards the ears, exhale down. Powerful breath. **3 minutes**.

5. Sit in Easy Pose, and do Ego Eradicator. Arms are at 60 degrees and fingers on the Venus mounds, thumbs point straight up. Breath of Fire. Focus above the head. **3 minutes**.
TO END: Inhale and hold the breath. Pull Mulbandh. Touch the thumbs above the head. Exhale. Repeat twice more. On the last exhalation, hold the breath out and sweep the aura as you bring your arms down. Relax.

Kriya for Pelvic Balance

1. Bridge Pose. Begin in a sitting position with the legs straight out.

a) Lean back slightly, supporting the upper torso with the arms locked at the elbows and the palms flat on the floor (fingertips facing the hips is recommended). Bending the knees, draw the feet in toward the hips with the soles flat against the floor.

b) Inhale and raise the hips so that the body—from the knees to the shoulders—forms a straight line parallel to the ground. Let the head fall back. The arms and the lower legs should be roughly at right angles to the body. Apply Mulbandh, hold the posture with normal breathing. Continue for **1-3 minutes**. Inhale. Exhale and relax.

This exercise strengthens the back and aids in metabolism.

2. Wheel Pose. Lie on the back. The legs should be bent with the soles of the feet pressed against the floor close to the hips.

a) Bending the elbows, place the palms of the hands on the floor behind the shoulders with the fingers pointing back toward the shoulders.

b) Inhale and carefully and comfortably raise the hips so that the body forms one continuous arch from the heels to the palms of the hands. Begin Breath of Fire. Continue for **1-3 minutes**. Inhale and slowly and carefully let yourself down and relax.

This exercise strengthens the lower back, facilitates the flow of energy through the spine and aids in metabolism.

3. Variation of Locust Pose. Lie on the stomach. Clasp the hands in Venus lock behind the back, interlocking the fingers. Inhale and raise the legs and arms as high as you can, keeping the knees and elbows straight and the legs together. Begin Breath of Fire. Continue for **1-3 minutes**. Inhale. Exhale and relax.

This exercise aids in digestion and strengthens the abdominal muscles.

Kriya for Pelvic Balance

4. Stand with your feet wide apart.

a) Raise the arms straight over the head with the palms pressed together. Inhale in this position, keeping the elbows and knees straight.

b) Exhale, bending at the waist, and touch the fingertips to the left foot. Inhale up once again and then exhale, bending at the waist and touching the right foot. Continue rhythmically with a powerful breath for **1-3 minutes**. Inhale in the upright position. Exhale and relax.

This exercise balances the movement of the pelvis and coordinates the muscle groups on opposite sides of the body.

5. Kundalini Lotus. Begin in a sitting position. Grasp the big toe of each foot with the thumb and the first two fingers of each hand, wrapping the fingers around the fleshy part of the toes with the thumbs pressed against the toenails. Raise the legs to an angle of 60 degrees to the floor, locking the knees. Spread the legs wide and keep the spine straight. Begin Breath of Fire. Continue for **1-3 minutes**. Inhale. Exhale and relax.

This exercise helps to channel sexual energy and maintain potency.

6. Come into Cow Pose, supporting the torso on the hands and knees.

a) Inhale, lifting the head up and back and raising the right leg as high as possible keeping the knees straight.

b) Exhale, bring the chin down to touch the chest and drawing the right knee toward the chest to touch the head. Then inhale back up into the original position.

Continue rhythmically with a powerful breath for **1-3 minutes**. Then inhale. Exhale and repeat the exercise on the opposite side. Continue for **1-3 minutes**. Then inhale. Exhale and relax.

This exercise balances the leg and abdominal muscles and helps to maintain sexual potency.

7. Deeply relax.

Tattvas, Pranic Rib Cage & Nervous System

1. Sit in Easy Pose with your spine straight. Keep the chin in and the chest out. Bend the elbows and support them on your rib cage with the palms facing toward the body. Allow the wrists to bend so the palms face upward, hands in front of the shoulders. Close the hands into fists and open them again rapidly and continuously. Put strength in your movement. **3 minutes**.

This creates an elementary balance, which is one of the most beautiful and powerful things of the human body. It will stimulate the basic tattvas...your breath will change. The pranic energy in the combination of your breath will change. You cannot buy that in the market, you have to produce it.

2. Still in Easy Pose, move the arms and shoulders like a bird in flight. Move fast. This balances both parts of the brain. Be sure that your shoulders move up and down with the movement of your arms. **3 minutes**.

This adjusts the ribs, is beneficial to the heart, and improves circulation in the chest area. This will help to adjust the ribs and balance both sides of the brain. However, if you start to feel nauseated, stop immediately.

Tattvas, Pranic Rib Cage & Nervous System

3. Sit in Easy Pose and look straight ahead. Alternate arm stretches. Move so that when the right hand extends forward and the left hand is back, the hands become fists, palm down. When the left hand is stretching forward and the right hand is back, the hands are open, relaxed and palm down. Move quickly and powerfully. The arms extend fully so that the elbow is straight. **3 minutes**.

This is for the nervous system. Move very fast so that the breath changes.

4. Bend the elbows with the palms facing forward, fingers slightly spread. Lean back 15 degrees. Close the eyes. Sit with the chin in and chest out. Balance your body from the chin, which is the Moon Center. Sing along with the recording *Meditation* by Wahe Guru Kaur and go into deep meditation. **15 minutes**.

The angle of the spine is important. If this exercise is done correctly, the basic psyche will change.

TO END: Inhale, lean back a little farther and stretch your spine vertebra by vertebra as you hold the breath **10-15 seconds**. Repeat this sequence two more times.

COMMENTS

Exercise one is for the *tattvas*, exercise two is for the pranic rib cage, and exercise three is for the nervous system.

Balancing Chakras & Corresponding Organs

1. Chair Pose with Breath of Fire. Begin in a standing position. Place the feet shoulder-width apart. Squat down so the thighs are parallel to the ground. Reach toward the toes, placing the palms on top of the feet by bringing the hands through the inside of the legs, around to the outside. Be sure to keep the back straight and lift only the head to look forward. **5 minutes.**

2. Sat Kriya. Sit on the heels and stretch the arms straight over the head so that the elbows hug the ears. Interlock the fingers except the index fingers, which point straight up. Begin to chant *Sat Naam* emphatically in a constant rhythm about 8 times per 10 seconds. Chant the sound *Sat* from the Navel Point and Solar Plexus, and pull the Navel all the way in and up, toward the spine. On *Naam* relax the belly. Continue very powerfully. To end, inhale and squeeze the muscles tightly from the buttocks all the way up the back, past the shoulders. **5 minutes.**

3. Sitting in Rock Pose on the heels, rest the hands on the thighs.

a) Begin Sitali Pranayam, inhaling in short sips through a curled tongue until the lungs are full of air.

b) Rotate the hips around in a circle. Hold the breath and rotate to the left for 1/2 the duration of the held breath. Then hold and rotate to the right for 1/2 the duration of the held breath. **3 times.**

4. In Victory Pose with the feet off the ground at a 60° angle and the torso raised off the ground at a 60° angle

a) Inhale and drop the torso and legs down to 45°

b) Exhale up to 60°. **5 minutes.**
If done properly, this is the equivalent of 8 hours of exercise.

5. Lie on the back and bring the hands to the Navel Point. The left hand is closest to the body and the right hand is over the left. There is about 2 inches between the body and also between the hands. Rotate the hands around each other in a clockwise direction, maintaining the 2-inch separation between the hands, and keeping the hands over the Naval Point. Long deep breathing. **3 minutes.**

6. Remain on your back and extend your arms up to 90°, straight above you. Make fists of your hands and with great tension, pull your fists into your chest. Release and repeat **2 more times**.

7. Rest on the back with the left hand on the heart and the right hand over the left. Long deep breathing—whispering *Ham Dam Haree Har Haree Har Ham Dam*. This is the meditation of the celestial angels. "God is my breath, breath is my God." **5 minutes**.

8. Sitting in Rock Pose, place hands in Bear Grip. One palm faces out from the chest with the thumb down. Place the palm of the other hand facing the chest. Bring the fingers together. Curl the fingers of both hands so the hands form a fist, where the fingers of one hand are hooked around the fingers of the other hand. The arms keep a steady pull at the heart. Move your elbows up and down, quickly. **11 minutes**.

9. Remain sitting on the heels, place the palms on the thighs and begin inhaling turning your head to the left, and exhaling turning your head to the right. **3 minutes**.

10. Come sitting in Easy Pose and bring the hands up to the face with the thumbs pressing on the temples. The fingers will be about 2 inches from the face. Roll the eyes up to the Third Eye Point, creating a pressure. Now chant: *Har Whaa-hay Guroo, Har Sat Naam*. **5 minutes**.
This mantra allows you to feel no pain at the time of death.

11. Prepare to sit on the heels but let the hips rest between the heels, touching the ground. Relax back down on the back with the hands by the sides. Do this as long as possible. Do not do it so long that any part of your body falls asleep.

12. Then relax on the back. **11-62 minutes**.

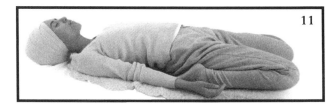

COMMENTS

You must stimulate your Navel Point once a day. If you do Breath of Fire, it will cleanse your lungs, make them strong, you will breathe deeply all day, you will have good oxygen in your bloodstream, and you will be young and healthy for a long time. If you do it 5-15 minutes every day, it is the best way to keep the blood purified. It's a direct blood purification system.

Releasing the Elements

1. In Easy Pose, with your elbows gently bent, dive the hands down and then extend the wrists up in a wave-like motion and then repeat—like waves of the ocean. It gives you the father principle: water. Use the entire arm to create the wave: shoulder, elbow and wrist. **8 minutes**.
TO END: Inhale deeply. Suspend the breath for 20 seconds. Exhale and relax.

Exactly one minute from now you will be upset. I can bet with you. In one minute more you will be upset, you will feel either angry or bored or you will feel both. This will do it. It is a very difficult exercise. . . you are working on a meridian here which connects with the liver, spleen and your whole immune system. You are directly dealing with your toxins and your poisons in the body.

2. Bring your hands in front of the chest. Make a tipi with your hands—fingers are slightly separated—and tap the fingertips together. You are playing with the five tattvas. All five fingertips meet at once. Move with the music. **4 minutes**.
Punjabi Drums was played in class.
TO END: Inhale deeply and suspend the breath for 30 seconds. Meditate at the Heart Center. Exhale.

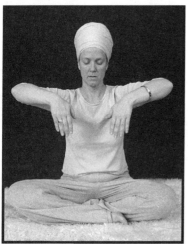

3. Bring the fingertips to the shoulders. Dance the shoulders like wings, any way you like, to the rhythm of the recording *Punjabi Drums*. Your spine will start adjusting and your lower back will hurt if it is out. After **2 minutes**, extend the tongue and begin heavy, long deep breathing through the mouth—Lion's Breath. Use the Navel—you're engaging the fire element. **5 minutes**. [**7 minutes** total]
TO END: Inhale deeply and suspend the breath for **15 seconds**. Exhale. Then inhale and suspend the breath for **10 seconds**. Exhale. Repeat.
Get your toxins out through the lungs—that is all you are doing. Tongue has to be out. That is the condition. Move the shoulders, move; break the calcium deposits. . . You are working with your air element and you are working with your fire element.

Releasing the Elements

4. Extend your arms up to the heavens. The arms are in a wide V, 45° above parallel, with the palms facing each another. Drop your head back and bring your gaze up to the sky. Listen to beautiful, inspiring music. **5 minutes**.
Nirinjan Kaur's Peace and Tranquility was played in class. Pray as your original self—the original man.

5. Place your hands on your heart—one hand resting on the other. Concentrate on what was the fontanel (the soft spot in the skull) in the crown of the head. Close your eyes. Try to become a little sparrow of time and space and project out. Leave the body and let it heal. Gong is played. **9-1/2 minutes**.

6. Hands still on the heart, inhale deeply and begin Breath of Fire.
3 minutes.
Nirinjan Kaur's Mera Man Lochai was played in class.
TO END: Inhale deeply and hold for 20 seconds, circulate the breath and focus on the area you want to heal. Quickly exhale and inhale. Concentrate as you suspend the breath for 15 seconds. Quickly exhale and inhale. Hold the breath for 15 seconds and concentrate on the area you want to heal. Exhale and relax.

COMMENTS
What do we want? Attention. The entire destructive behavior and improper human dialogue is because we want attention— and we get it by either behaving good or bad. It is stressful. We have to become a stress-free zone. We have to deeply understand that being free of stress is the source or key to happiness.

Synchronizing the Brain & the Tattvas

1. Sit in Virasan and place the palms together at the sternum. Extend the left arm out to the side, 60 degrees above parallel, palm facing down, and move the left hand up and down at the wrist as fast as possible, keeping the elbow locked. Coordinate the movement with Breath of Fire for **3 minutes**. Change arms and continue for **3 minutes**.

2. Extend both arms and resume the motion with both arms for **2 minutes**. Close your eyes and visualize yourself flying high in the sky. Take yourself through the five elements and totally identify with each.

   First imagine you are ether, then air, then fire, then water, then earth, then ether again. Feel the difference between each, especially when you return to the ether. Spend about 15 seconds on each tattva.

This exercise helps differentiate the left from the right hemispheres of the brain. Normally Breath of Fire creates a neutral state. Here, however, the movement of the hands creates that differentiation and synchronizes the hemispheres as well. Additionally, this exercise is said to balance the tattvas. For optimum results, practice it every day.

3. Sit in Easy Pose. Make fists of the hands with the thumbs tucked inside, and place them palm down in front of the chest at the level of the heart. Now, without moving the wrists, rotate the fists rapidly around each other in coordination with Breath of Fire for **1 minute**.

COMMENTS

As explained in Yogic philosophy, all living matter is comprised of five elements: earth, air, fire, water and ether. These are known as the five tattvas. Practice of this short kriya will bring the tattvas into a state of balance and will synchronize the hemispheres of the brain. This is a very powerful set of exercises to practice every day.

Meditation to Command the Five Tattvas

Sit very straight. Listen to the mantra:

Aap sahaaee hoaa
Sachay daa sachaa doaa
Har, har, har

The Lord Himself has become our protector,
the Truest of the True has taken care of us.
God, God, God.

When you hear the word Har, pull the navel point in. For the three words of *Har*, your breath will become a 3-stroke breath of fire. Then suspend the breath out as you keep the navel point pulled in and listen to the rest of the mantra. Just before the *Har* sounds come again, inhale quickly and repeat the breath stroke cycle again.

TIME: **62 minutes**. To use the Naad to imprint your mind, do this meditation daily for 90 days. Then you will know the practical experience and power and miracle of the spoken word.

COMMENTS

This mantra meditation from the Siri Guru Granth Sahib is a gift to you that will let you penetrate into the Unknown without fear. It will give you protection and mental balance. It is very simple and rhythmic. If you do it very nobly it will be extremely helpful. Whenever you are effective and create a success in your life, you must also generate some opposition and animosity. That is called the Law of Polarity. It is called facing a square in your life. This meditation will totally eliminate enemies and block the impact of animosity forever. It can give you mental self-control and let you command your five tattvas for effective living.

Stimulate Your Chakras

Sit in Easy Pose.

MUDRA: Put the fingers of your left hand on your forehead touching your Third Eye Point, placing the Mercury finger at the Brow Point and stacking the remaining fingers up the midline of the forehead. Extend your right arm out straight forward from your shoulder with the palm facing left.

EYES: Close your eyes, hold the position.

BREATH: Breathe slowly and deeply, and meditate silently. Recharge your body with energy.

TIME: **18 minutes**.

TO END: Inhale, hold your breath **5-10 seconds**, and exhale. Repeat this sequence one more time. Then inhale, hold your breath **10-15 seconds**, and, with your fingers interlocked over your head, stretch your spine upward. Exhale and relax.

COMMENTS

This kriya is for handling the pressures of the Information Age. As you do the posture, your breathing will change. Use your breath, the energy of prana, to carry you through. Keep your right arm stretched out parallel to the ground, to catch up with the magnetic field of the earth. Your left hand is at your pituitary to balance the heavens. The force of your breath will become longer and more powerful. Your body will start feeling pain. This pain will give you endurance, endurance will cause you to rise above your situations, and, once you rise above yourself, you've got it.

"This life is not for wasting. It is for reaching the wonderlands of your own consciousness."

Sit straight. Place the palms together at the center of the chest, thumbs touching the center of the sternum. With the eyes closed focus at the brow point. Inhale deeply. With the exhale chant a long *Sat* with a short *Naam*. Vibrate *Sat* in 6 waves, with *Naam* forming the seventh. On each wave, thread the sound up through the chakras beginning at the base of the spine. On *Naam* project the sound through the crown of the head to Infinity. As the sound penetrates each chakra, gently pull the physical area of the body it corresponds to (i.e. rectum, sex organs, navel point, heart, throat, brow point, and crown of the head).

Sat Naam

Sat Naam means "My identity is Truth, I vibrate with the Truth"

TIME: Continue for **11 to 31 minutes**.

COMMENTS

This meditation will give you balance and clear intuition. If you know your purpose and goal, you can discern what is useful and what is not. Every coincidence is a larger pattern in action. Relax and see beyond the surface to catch useful currents and be in the best position to act intelligently. Note: The sound is not created in the throat; but rather by the pulling on the chakras and their organs as the sound ascends the spine. One should be able to hear the waves of sound as it rises along the spine.

High Tech Yoga

...in Easy Pose with a straight spine, and a light Neck Lock.

EYES: Eyes are closed.

MANTRA & MUDRA: Chant along with the *Rakhe Rakhanhar* mantra and move in the following sequence of mudras. This is a series of 8 mudras relating to the eight chakras, corresponding to the lines of the mantra. Change at each line of the mantra. *(Singh Kaur's recording of the mantra is recommended.)*

TIME: **127 minutes**.

Rakhay rakhanhaar aap ubaarian
Gyan Mudra (thumb to index finger):
wrists rest on knees, palms facing outward.

Gur kee pairee paa-eh kaaj savaarian
Gyan Mudra: with hands in the lap, palms up.

Hoaa aap dayaal manho na visaarian
Shuni Mudra (thumb to middle finger):
with fingers pressed at the navel area.

Saadh janaa kai sang bhavjal taarian
Surya Mudra (thumb to ring finger):
with fingers pressed at the Heart Center.

High Tech Yoga

Saakat nindak dusht khin maa-eh bidaarian

Buddhi Mudra (thumb to little finger): with fingers pressed below ears facing towards the back of the neck.

Tis saahib kee tayk naanak manai maa-eh

Both hands over the face, fingertips along hairline.

Jis simrat sukh ho-eh saglay dookh jaa-eh

Interlock fingers on top of the head.

Jis simrat sukh ho-eh saglay dookh jaa-eh

Extend arms out straight at 45 degrees with palms up.

COMMENTS

In this kriya, we experience the movement and flow between the chakras. It is through our chakras that we gain access and power to shift gears and respond at a higher frequency to varied circumstances. This is one of the fundamental fruits of practice and a true mark of the beginning of mastery of the Self. To be able to move our energy from the heart to the navel and back again in order to express compassion, or power, or love is the measure of our neutrality and a sign of our ability to be authentic in each moment.

Kirtan Kriya[1]

This kriya is one of three that Yogi Bhajan mentioned would carry us through the Aquarian Age, even if all other teachings were lost. There are four principle components to practicing Kirtan Kriya correctly: Mantra, Mudra, Voice, and Visualization.

POSTURE: Sit in Easy Pose with a straight spine, and a light Neck Lock.

EYES: Focus at the Brow Point.

MANTRA: This kriya uses the five primal sounds, or the Panj Shabd— S, T, N, M, A—in the original bij (seed) form of the mantra *Sat Nam*:

SAA — Infinity, cosmos, beginning
TAA — Life, existence
NAA — Death, change, transformation
MAA — Rebirth

This is the cycle of creation. From the Infinite comes life and individual existence. From life comes death or change. From death comes the rebirth of consciousness. From rebirth comes the joy of the Infinite through which compassion leads back to life. Chant the 'A' like 'mom,' in the following manner:

Each repetition of the entire mantra takes 3 to 4 seconds.

SAA TAA NAA MAA

MUDRA: The elbows are straight while chanting, beginning with hands in Gyan Mudra. Each finger touches, in turn, the tip of the thumb with a firm but gentle pressure.

SAA — Press the Jupiter (index) finger and thumb.
TAA — Press the Saturn (middle) finger and thumb.
NAA — Press the Sun (ring) finger and thumb.
MAA — Press the Mercury (pinkie) finger and thumb.

Begin again with the index finger.

 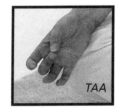 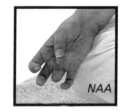 

VOICE

The mantra is chanted in the three languages of consciousness:

Aloud (the voice of the human) — awareness of the things of the world
Whisper (the voice of the lover) — experiencing the longing to belong
Silent (the voice of the divine) — meditate on Infinity or mentally vibrate

[1] pronounced "keertan Kreeya"

VISUALIZATION

Visualize the flow of the sounds in an "L" form. As you meditate feel there is a constant inflow of cosmic energy into your solar center (Tenth Gate, the Crown Chakra). As the energy enters the top of the head, you flow the sounds *Saa, Taa, Naa, Maa* through. As you chant *SAA* for example, the "S" starts at the top of the head and the "A" moves down and out through the Brow Point, projected to Infinity. This energy flow follows the energy pathway called the Golden Cord—the connection between the pineal and pituitary gland. Some people may occasionally experience headaches from practicing Kirtan Kriya if they do not use this "L" form. The most common reason for this is improper circulation of prana in the solar centers.

TO BEGIN THE PRACTICE

Sit straight in Easy Pose and meditate at the Brow Point.

Chant aloud for 5 minutes.

Then whisper for 5 minutes.

Then go deeply into silence, mentally vibrating the sound for 10 minutes.

Then whisper for 5 minutes.

Then chant aloud for 5 minutes.

TO END: Close the meditation with a deep inhale and suspend the breath as long as comfortable—up to a minute—relaxing it smoothly to complete **1 minute** of absolute stillness and silence. Then, stretch the hands up as far as possible and spread the fingers wide. Stretch the spine and take several deep breaths. Relax.

COMMENTS

Practicing this meditation brings a total mental balance to the individual psyche. As you vibrate on each fingertip, you alternate your electrical polarities. The index and ring fingers are electrically negative, relative to the other fingers. This causes a balance in the electro-magnetic projection of the aura. If during the silent part of the meditation your mind wanders uncontrollably, go back to a whisper, to a loud voice, to a whisper and back into silence. Do this as often as necessary to stay alert.

Each time the mudra is closed by joining the thumb with a finger, the ego "seals" the effect of that mudra in the consciousness. The effects are as follows:

SIGN	FINGER	NAME	EFFECT
Jupiter	Index	Gyan Mudra	Knowledge
Saturn	Middle	Shuni Mudra	Wisdom, intelligence,patience
Sun	Ring	Surya Mudra	Vitality, energy of life
Mercury	Pinkie	Buddhi Mudra	Ability to communicate

Practicing this meditation is both a science and an art. It is an art in the way it molds consciousness and the refinement of sensation and insight it produces. It is a science in the tested certainty of the results it produces. This meditation is based on the tested experience of many people, in many conditions, over many years. It is based on the structure of the psyche and the laws of action and reaction that accompany each sound, movement and posture. Chanting the Panj Shabd—the primal or nuclear form of *Sat Naam*—has profound energy within it because we are breaking the bij (seed or atom) of the sound into its primary elements.

The timing can be decreased or increased as long as you maintain the ratio of spoken, whispered, and silent chanting—always end with 1 minute of complete stillness and silence. Yogi Bhajan has said that a person who wears pure white and meditates on this sound current for 2 1/2 hours a day for one year, will know the Unknown and see the Unseen. Through this constant practice, the mind awakens to the infinite capacity of the soul for sacrifice, service, and creation.

Being Human: Balancing Heaven & Earth

1a&b

1c

Sit in Easy Pose with a straight spine.

MUDRA: The right arm is up with the right elbow and forearm on the same plane as the shoulder. The right arm makes a perfect 90 degree angle and the palm faces down toward the Earth. The left hand is parallel to the right with the palm facing the sky. Keep the fingers together and very stiff and tight throughout.

EYES: Eyes are at the tip of the nose.

BREATH:

1a) Long Deep Breathing. Breathe mechanically, not automatically. **9 minutes**.

1b) Begin squeezing the entire body as you breathe. Continue breathing very mechanically, rhythmically. It will stimulate your psyche. **1 1/2 minutes**.

1c) Lion's Breath. Stick your tongue out and breathe through your mouth, mechanically breathing. Continue holding the mudra and squeezing the entire body. **2 minutes**.

2. a) Put your hands in your lap and sit straight and breathe very calmly. Meditate deeply. Go into thoughtlessness. *Har Singh Nar Singh* recording by Nirinjan Kaur is played. **6 1/2 minutes**.
If you want any achievement in your life, go into thoughtlessness so that you can be you. There is no other way. Right now, denounce the thought.

b) *Sat Nam Wahe Guru.* (A rhythmic version of this mantra can be played.) Pump the navel with the mantra, breathing voluntarily, mechanically, not allowing the posture to change. Pump the navel fairly quickly with the beat. Breath should be absolutely mechanical. Exhaling with each pump of the navel. Let your navel dance. **4 minutes**.

TO END: Inhale deep. Cannon Fire exhale. **3 times**. On the third repetition, squeeze the body and hold the breath a little longer and then Cannon Fire out. Be seated for a while and don't try to get up.

CHAPTER FIVE

DHYANA, DHARANA
& PRATYAHAR

MASTERING THE SELF

Cultivating the Neutral Mind

"How can we transfer people from nothing to every-thing? Are we magicians, do we have some magic drug? What is the formula behind it? It is very simple: man is a meditative animal; there is simply a deficiency in the glandular system, period."

–Yogi Bhajan

Concentration, meditation and mastery of the senses are the things we think of when we imagine the yogi in the cave on the mountain. *Dhyana, dharana* and *pratyahar* are the foundation practices of a yogi, and they apply to our householder path as well. *Shuniya*—the still point—is the fountain, the well spring, from which all the blessings of meditation come. From emptiness, everything comes. The capacity to dwell in *shuniya* and to act in consciousness are the the hallmarks of a yogi. *Shuniya* is the seat of transformation, outside of time and space. These are the practices where we refine our core identity through the lens of *shuniya*—the Neutral Mind.

"How can we transfer people from nothing to everything? Are we magicians, do we have some magic drug? What is the formula behind it? It is very simple: man is a meditative animal; there is simply a deficiency in the glandular system, period.

I asked someone, "What is your problem?"

He told me, "My problem is I don't work."

"Do you want to work?"

He said, "No."

"Is there any chance?"

He said, "No chance."

"Why have you come to me?"

He said, "With all my hardship and labor and work, I came to you because I understand you change people."

I said, "No, I don't change people, people change themselves."

He said, "Well, doesn't matter, question is, I want to change."

I said, "The only problem is that those who want change, they never change, with you it will be a hardship."

"Why?"

"Because you want to change in your style; I am going to change with my style; so there is already a clash. . . . If you had said "I have no intention to change", I would have convinced you that life is nothing but a law of change and you would have done it. Now the problem is, you want to change and I want to change you, but you want to change at your own frequency. There is nothing wrong with any one's mind. Instead, there is a basic misunderstanding in what you call happiness. If the changes are at the frequency you want, then you are happy; and if they are at a different frequency you are unhappy—that decides your happiness and unhappiness."

–Yogi Bhajan, April 11, 1976

These kriyas deliver the practitioner to *Dhyana, Dharana* and *Pratyahar*, which in turn deliver the capacity to change frequencies, to invite new patterns, and to cultivate a meditative mind. As long as we continue to label things "good" and "bad", we will continue to be unhappy. Cultivating the Neutral Mind allows us to see beyond the labels and to experience insight, intuition and awakening. Invoking a Meditative State initiates the prana and awakens the kundalini. Parbati's Kriya brings you to the Blue Pearl, the flame at the tip of the nose. Ganesha Meditation for Focus and Clarity projects the focus of the Third Eye. Meditation for the Neutral Mind along with the Kriya and Meditation for Thoughtlessness deliver a state of emptiness, the thought waves of the mind become still, the mind rests in a state of thoughtlessness.

Sitalee Uni Kriya is one of the most profound and explicit meditations for *pratyahar*. You physically close down the doors to the senses: the eyes and the ears. Apply conscious breathing and the state of pratyahar entrains the mind to a state of stillness. The final meditation in this chapter is a simple, efficient way to reach a state of relaxation.

Relaxation is the key to happiness. When we deeply relax, we create the conditions for the kundalini to spontaneously arise. Joy, equanimity and repose are the fruits of deep meditation. Transformation becomes possible. The changes you've always longed to manifest naturally arise from the state of *shuniya*, and these core disciplines make up the root of our practice because they lead us on the path of transformation and help us to realize our identity, as practitioners and yogis.

Meditation for the Neutral Mind

Sit in Easy Pose with the spine straight.

MUDRA: Put both hands in the lap with the palms facing up. Rest the right hand into the left. The thumb tips may touch or not. Remove all tension from every part of the body. Sit straight by achieving a balance.

EYES: Eyes are closed.

BREATH & FOCUS: Imagine seeing your self sitting peacefully and full of radiance. Then gradually let your energy collect like a flow at the brow point. Let the breath regulate itself into a meditative slow, almost suspended, manner. Concentrate without effort at that point and mentally vibrate in a simple monotone, as if chopping the sound, projecting each syllable distinctly:

Whaa-hay Gu-roo
Infinite identity from darkness to light.

Call on the higher self and keep going steadily through all barriers.
Let go and let God.

TIME: **11 to 31 minutes.**

COMMENTS
It is easy to hear a truth and difficult to live it, to embed it deeply into your heart and mind. The Neutral Mind opens the gate to that deep remembrance of the self and soul. *Jappa* done with the refined Neutral Mind leads to *Naam chit aveh*: It lets all other thoughts be without disturbance to your constant inner light. The Neutral Mind lives for the touch of vastness.

Sit with the spine straight, with Neck Lock.

MUDRA: Relax the right shoulder, elbow by the side, hand straight out, palm facing up. The palm is not flat, but rather has a little dip or depth. The left arm is parallel to the ground with the palm facing up, touching the diaphragm at the lower chest area.

The left hand will separate Prana and Apana at the point of Uddiyana. Refuse to think. Become thoughtless. Be thoughtless. Let everything go.

MUSIC: Singh Kaur's *Guru Ram Das* was used in class. Any transcendant music can be used.

EYES: Eyes are closed.

RHYTHM & BREATH: One Minute Breath: Inhale 20 seconds, hold 20 seconds, exhale 20 seconds.

TIME: **11 minutes**.

TO END: Inhale, hold 25 seconds while pressing the left hand against the diaphragm. Squeeze the entire body. Exhale. Inhale, hold 25 seconds and bring all the energy over that point. Don't spare your diaphragm line, as you squeeze the body. Exhale. Inhale the last time. Hold 25 seconds, squeeze the body and apply pressure with the left hand as if you were going to touch the spinal column through the rib cage. Exhale and relax.

COMMENTS

If you don't think that there is a challenge in your life then you have no life. Life without challenge doesn't exist. Challenge is that which is answered by you, and that answer by you is by your qualification. So you have to qualify. Let us go to the medulla right here and get to the third ring of the brain stem so that we can reorganize our neurological system so we can be in our intuitive awareness. That's how, in another fifty years, life is going to be. All this knowledge you have so far is bogus. It doesn't work, doesn't qualify.

When you come to the state of thoughtlessness, then the Master Mind of the Universe starts serving you. Man becomes a god and god becomes servant. The polarity reverses itself by just becoming thoughtless. Start qualifying your thoughts. The moment you start qualifying your thoughts, you will start purifying your being, and a purified being becomes the temple of the spirit and then all shakti, all powers, all prakirti, come and serve... Otherwise you are on sale.

—YOGI BHAJAN

Kriya for Thoughtlessness

1. Sit with a straight spine. Palms face forward, elbows at the side. Lock the Mercury finger with the thumb (id or ego) in Buddhi Mudra. Bend it very tightly. The rest of the fingers are straight. Make circles with the hands—180 times per minute; the hands circle toward the outside. The movement is very fast—about three times per second. **8 minutes.**

TO END: Inhale deep. Squeeze the shoulders tightly together and push the chest forward, while holding the hands in the mudra at the sides of your shoulders, palms facing forward. Release the shoulders, bend forward and exhale. Repeat twice more.

2. Curl the tongue and breathe through the mouth—Sitali Pranayam—throughout this next exercise. Bring the hands in front of you, palms down, one hand over the other and begin making circles—180 revolutions per minute. Keep the hands at the level of the navel point and slightly apart. Fingertips point toward opposite elbows and the hands move in circles toward the torso. **8 minutes.**

TO END: Inhale deeply. Squeeze the shoulders tightly together and push the chest forward. Release the shoulders, come forward and exhale. Repeat twice more.

This exercise can help take away headaches. Create a magnetic field with your hands. This breath is very cooling and good for the kidneys and for the adrenals. It is absolutely wonderful for urinary system, and for testosterone, and most helpful to the pituitary.

Kriya for Thoughtlessness

3. Close the eyes. Bring your hands in front of the heart center—palms down, right hand resting on the left—and just balance and be steady. **15 minutes**.

TO END: Inhale deep. Squeeze the shoulders tightly together and push the chest forward. Release the shoulders, bend forward and exhale. Repeat twice more.

You won't feel tired, you won't feel heavy, you won't feel anything. . . . Close your eyes and just have no thought. Entertain no thought. Stay in a thoughtless state. I repeat, you are in a habit to hypnotize yourself. So please hypnotize yourself in a thoughtless state, 'I am, I am not' at the same time. Create a vacuum to allow prosperity, real happiness and infinity to enter.

4. Chant with the recording of *Har Singh Nar Singh* by Nirinjan Kaur. Use the tip of the tongue **9 minutes**.

Har singh nar singh neel naaraayan
Gursikh gur singh har har gayan
Wha-hay guroo Wha-hay guroo, har har dhiayan
Saakhat nindak dusht mathaayan

God the Protector takes care of the universe.

Those who live in God consciousness and power, chant Har Har.

Meditate on Wahe Guru and live in that ecstasy.

Those who vibrate God's Name and relate to God, all karmas are cleared.

TO END: Inhale deep. Squeeze the shoulders together and push the chest forward. Release the shoulders, bend forward, exhale and relax.

Parbati's Kriya

1. Sit in a very easy, graceful posture with a straight spine, chin in, chest out. Eyes are at the tip of the nose. When the eyes are at the correct angle, (about 60 degrees) you should see a little blue circle—a "slice of the moon." Don't lose sight of it. Turn your tongue and press it into the upper palate. Keep your molars locked. Watch your breath—concentrate on both nostrils (the ending points of *ida* and *pingala*) and breathe gracefully and consciously. Concentrate. Be alert. Remain absolutely still. Do not move. **11 minutes**.

TO END: Inhale deeply and focus at the brow. Hold the breath and contract. **15 seconds**. Exhale. Repeat twice more. Relax.

2. Bring your fingertips together and press the fingers in and out making circles with them. Expand and contract. Wiggle the toes, too, in a circular manner. **1 1/2 minutes**.

3. Stretch the legs out in front of you. Make your hands into claws, in front of the shoulders. Flex the ankle and the toes toward your head. Stretch the Achilles tendon. Lock the molars. **3 minutes**.
Your fingers have to be steel claws and your toes must come backward at the maximum. Be steady.

4. With your arms supporting you, look toward the sky and laugh with a very open mouth. Keep the neck extended and the face up. **2 minutes**.

5. Now lock your lips together and shake your head very quickly. This is a very small but rapid movement from side to side. **15 seconds**.

6. Talk, relax and visit each other.

Ganesha Meditation for Focus & Clarity

Sit with a straight spine and the eyes closed.

MUDRA: The left thumb and little finger extend out from the hand. The other fingers are curled into a fist with fingertips on the Moon Mound (the root of the thumb that extends down to the wrist).

1a) The left hand and elbow are parallel to the floor, with the tip of the left thumb pressing on the curved notch of the nose between the eyes.

1b) With the right hand and elbow parallel to the floor, grasp the left little finger with the right hand and close the right hand into a fist around it, so that both hands now extend straight out from your head. Push the notch with the tip of the left thumb to the extent that you feel some soreness as you breathe long and deep. After continued practice, this soreness reduces.

TIME: Do this for **3 minutes** and no longer. With practice you can extend this meditation up to **11 minutes**. But if you've mastered it, you only need **3 minutes** for immediate focus and to stop the negative thought that was taking you where you did not want to go.

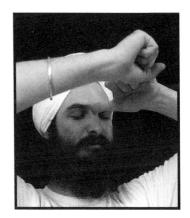

TO END: Maintain the posture with eyes closed, inhale. Push a little more and pull the Navel Point in by tightening the abdominal muscles for **10 seconds**, then exhale. Repeat one more time.

Sitalee Uni Kriya

Note: This kriya should be practiced in the evening only. A citrus fast beginning at 12 pm should be practiced prior to practicing this kriya.

1. Sit in Easy Pose with a straight spine, chin in, and chest lifted. Place your hands on the gates of your face in Shanmukhi Mudra. *(See comments.)* Whistle along with the music of *Sat Nam, Wahe Guru Indian version #2.* Whistle both on the inhalation and on the exhalation. **31 minutes.**

Use the whistle with a double force: out and in. Do not put pressure on your fingers in the mudra, keep your touch on the gates light and polite.

2. Relax the hands and take the fingers off your face. Remain sitting and begin shaking every part of your body as fast as you can. (This exercise was done to the rhythm of the *Bhangra Rhythms* tape.) **5 1/2 minutes.**

Use power, use strength, use projection and imagination. Be creative. Dance your body away. Let the circulation (flow); let the nervous system put a combination. You must bring the body to a sweat. If you do not sweat you will lose this best chance to be young.

TO END: Inhale deeply, hold your breath for **15 seconds** while stretching the body upward. Spread the fingers apart, letting the five tattwas balance themselves. Make the fingers like steel prongs. Exhale. Inhale deeply, hold the breath (**5-10 seconds**), repeat the stretch. Exhale. Last time: inhale deeply, hold the breath (**5-10 seconds**), and repeat the stretch. Exhale and relax.

Sitalee Uni Kriya

COMMENTS

This is a rare secret kriya of the very inner essence of sacred yoga, using Shanmukhi Mudra (delicately touching the seven gates in the head to help us focus on the inner world): Raise the arms in front of the face with the elbows pointing out to the sides. Place the thumbs gently on the Sun point of the ears (from the earlobe down, "those little things which the master pulls when you do wrong"); place the Jupiter (index) fingers lightly and delicately on the closed eyelids; place the Saturn (middle) fingers lightly on each side of the tip of the nose (where the *Ida* and *Pingala* end); place the Sun (ring) fingers on the upper lips and place the Mercury (pinkie) fingers on the lower lips.

These are the most delicate points in your whole body. Now look straight through your closed eyelids and create a screen. Bring your body to a standstill. This is just an acupuncture touch. It is just a very light, polite touch because the five antennas and five *tattvas* (earth, air, water, fire and ether) have to be balanced. That is all it is. The heat of the Sun point is in the earlobes. Upper eyelid is for the simple sense of the ether. *Ida* and *Pingala* (the nostrils) is the prana (air *tattva*). The upper lip is water and lower lip is earth. All these *tattvas* can be experienced within the body. You may feel irritated in this position, but focus on the achievement. . . . And tomorrow (after doing this kriya) you will not be the same as you are today. There is no way. That is a gospel truth.

Invoking a Meditative State

Sit in Easy Pose with a straight spine.

MUDRA: Make a solid fist of the right hand and raise it up to shoulder level with the forearm parallel to the spine. Raise the left hand up until the wrist is at shoulder level and the forearm is parallel to the spine. Bend the wrist so that the palm faces upward and the fingers point to the left. The fingers are straight and the palm is flat.
Consciously hold the hand positions. The left hand will want to move from its position, but keep it steady. Honest effort will bring the best results in experience.

EYES: Look at the tip of the nose.

BREATH: Inhale deeply in a long, slow, complete manner. Completely exhale with the same kind of conscious, controlled breath. Hold the breath out to your maximum; when you can no longer hold the breath out without straining, inhale deeply. Continue this breath pattern.

TIME: Begin with **11 minutes** and slowly and gradually build up to a maximum of **31 minutes**.

TO END: Rapidly inhale and exhale twice (**2 seconds** inhale, **2 seconds** exhale) and then inhale, hold the breath in for **10 seconds**, and stretch both hands up and tighten the body. Exhale and relax.

COMMENTS

Just experience this meditation. It affects the pituitary and glandular system and its impulsation of clockwise and anti-clockwise spin. Kundalini Yoga is a systematic method of glandular control through which the pituitary's relationship with consciousness is stimulated to invoke a meditative state in us.

The mind and emotions will keep repeating unless interrupted. The stress you generate with each thought, even subconsciously, narrows and binds you to a reactive pattern. This meditation helps you to gain mastery over your experience and breaks through the mystery of why things happen to you. It gives you strength, and the ability to engage openly in the challenges of life so they become opportunities; markers along the way to expressing your soul's true purpose. Stop rejecting life out of fear and begin to see how the Infinite reveals Itself to you in each moment, each relationship, and each word.

Meditation to Feel Calm & Cozy

Sit in a meditative posture.

MUDRA: Connect the tips of the thumb and middle finger of the right hand and the thumb and pinky of the left. The fingernails don't touch. (Females reverse the mudra in each hand.) With the shoulders relaxed, hold the hands 7-8 inches apart, fingers pointing forward, just in front of the nipples.

EYES: The eyes are 1/10 open.

BREATH: Breathe normally and meditate.

TIME: **11 minutes**

TO END: Inhale and lift both hands a bit and move them round and round quickly, for the length of the breath. Repeat twice more and relax.

COMMENTS

This meditation will create within us a sensitivity, and a prosperous mental horizon. It will create a calm and cozy feeling, even under the pressures of our minds and the changes of the Age. It strengthens the nervous system and develops a steadiness to act intelligently.

CHAPTER SIX

CLEARING THE SUBCONSCIOUS

MASTERING THE SELF

Accessing the True Self

"Conscious action raises the consciousness, habitual action raises the habit. So when you do something under an impulse, you become impulsive and compulsive; you lose your will. When you do not have your will, you cannot recognize God's will—and that's the way it goes, folks."

–Yogi Bhajan

The ego is here to serve us, but just as we must train the mind in order to make it into our faithful servant; so, too, the ego must be trained and aligned to the soul's purpose, our True Identity. Otherwise, it simply plays out all of our unresolved subconscious agendas and uses our anger, pain, childhood resentments and phobias to serve its own ends. You've got to admire the ego's fortitude as it strives, against all odds, to get attention and recognition. This unending quest for attention and recognition is one addiction we all share. It must have it at any cost, and it will take it in any form it can get. Praise is welcomed, but if that's not available, the ego will accept sympathy, and if that's not available then abuse will do. Its hunger is insatiable. No matter how much attention it gets, it's never enough. It eats and eats and eats but can never be satisfied. Guru Nanak Dev Ji, initiator of Sikh Dharma, put it this way, "... and the hunger of the hungry can never be relieved."

The ego is housed in a body that is but a speck of animated matter, on this tiny dot of rock we call Earth, hidden in a far corner of a minor galaxy in a seemingly unending universe. Add to that equation the billions of other tiny animated objects that garner more attention, accumulate more wealth, or worse, even become famous—and let's face it, it's a recipe for disappointment. No matter how hard we strive, we simply never get the respect we are due; or the status we believe we have earned; or the love we think we deserve. No wonder everyone seems so angry!

Anger expresses itself in a variety of ways: your anger may bubble up to the surface of your personality, ready to explode at the slightest hint of provocation; or, terrified by this wild uncontrollable force, you might control your anger by dominating it with your rational mind, which always finds reasons to calm you down and explain away your frustrations; or you might simply keep it veiled by a thin veneer of civility and social manners. But when you scratch the surface, you are really angry! No matter how hard you try to cover for it or control it, your anger is going to express itself . And no matter how it expresses itself—overtly or covertly, consciously or unconsciously, externally or internally—that anger is going to harm you.

"When you are angry, your entire energy consolidates into the wavelength of the angry thought; you stay in anger perpetually. Your anger takes away nourishment from your body, takes away heat from your stomach and energy from your circulation. If you realized the cost for even one moment of anger, you would never become angry."

–Yogi Bhajan, March 1, 1988

Why does it stay with us perpetually? Because it becomes engrained in our psyche as a neurosis. Yogi Bhajan gave us a simple formula to understand this: ego plus anger equals neurosis. Neuroses are habitual reaction patterns. When we're confronted by life's challenges, our neuroses are triggered automatically, which sets off a series of actions and reactions, a sequence of cause and effect we call the "wheel of karma". Trapped in our own particular self-fulfilling prophecies, which bring us back, again and again, to the same point, confronting the same situation over and over, with the same results, which cause the same effect *ad infinitum*; our neuroses lock us into a circular pattern. Like a hamster on its wheel, we find ourselves spinning the wheel of karma and never getting anywher

So your ego is an attention-seeking junkie, who will do anything to get the attention but will never be satisfied no matter how much it gets, which causes frustration that in turn triggers anger, which creates a neurotic pattern that traps you, over and over again. Luckily there is some good news: You are not your ego. The essence of your being is a little piece of God we call the soul. If you identify your Self with your soul, then the fire tattva, often expressed as anger, transforms into will power, which you can use to break the karmic cycle of cause and effect. By consciously acting, instead of unconsciously reacting to the challenges of life, your ego is given the chance to perform its most important functions: individuation, protection and survival. The ego is your fundamental survival mechanism whose job is to create an individual identity for you, providing boundaries, information and motivation to get you what you need. This is the recipe for consciousness: soul plus will power equals consciousness.

"Conscious action raises the consciousness, habitual action raises the habit. So when you do something under an impulse, you become impulsive and compulsive; you lose your will. When you do not have your will, you cannot recognize God's will—and that's the way it goes, folks."

–Yogi Bhajan, December 25, 1978

The kriyas and meditations in this chapter work to balance the Negative Mind, strengthen the Navel Point, release pent up frustration, clear out old phobias, and align your Self with your soul. Once the static has cleared, the emotions have calmed, and the commotions have died down then we can release our subconscious mind of its negative habits and experience that neutral state of consciousness we call the meditative mind. With this, we access our True Self and become aware of *Sat Nam*, our True Identity.

Kriya to Relieve Inner Anger

1. Lie down flat on the back in a relaxed posture with the arms at your sides, palms open and legs slightly apart. Pretend to snore for **1 1/2 minutes**.

2. Still lying on the back, keep the legs straight; raise both legs up to 6 inches and hold for **2 minutes**. This exercise balances anger. It pressurizes the navel to balance the whole system.

3. Remaining in the posture with your legs up at 6 inches, stick out your tongue and do Breath of Fire through your mouth for **1 1/2 minutes**.

4. Still lying on the back, lift the legs up to 90 degrees. The arms are on the ground by the sides. Begin to beat the ground with all the anger you can achieve. Beat hard and fast for **2 1/2 minutes**, keeping the arms stiff and straight.

5. Still on the back, bring the knees up to the chest, and stick the tongue out. Inhale through the open mouth and exhale through the nose. Continue for **3 minutes**.

6. Sit in Celibate Pose with the buttocks on the floor between the heels. Cross the arms over the chest and press them hard against the rib cage. Bend forward and touch the forehead to the floor as if you are bowing. For **2 1/2 minutes** move at a pace of approximately 30 bows per minute, then for another **30 seconds** speed up and move as fast as you can.

Kriya to Relieve Inner Anger

7. Sitting with the legs straight out in front, begin to beat all the parts of your body with open palms. Move fast for **2 minutes**.

8. Stand up, bend forward, keeping the back parallel to the ground, and let the arms and hands hang loose. Remain in this posture and sing for **3 minutes**. (In class, Yogi Bhajan played a recording of *Guru Guru Wahe Guru, Guru Ram Das Guru*.)

9. Continue singing and come into Cobra Pose, keeping the elbows straight and stretching the spine. Continue for **1 minute**. Begin circling the neck and continue to sing for another **30 seconds**.

10. Still in Cobra Pose begin kicking the ground with alternate feet for **30 seconds**.

11. Sit in Easy Pose and close the eyes. Stretch the arms over the head, keeping the elbows straight, and interlace the fingers with the index fingers extended and pointing straight up. Begin Sat Kriya for **3 minutes**.

12. Lie down and nap in Corpse Pose on the back for **5 minutes**.

Unloading the Subconscious

1. Sit in Easy Pose with Christ Mudra. Hold down Sun and the Mercury fingers with the thumb; bend the elbows and hold the mudra at the shoulders with the palms facing forward. Open the jaw wide and inhale in three quick strokes; exhale through the nose. **6 minutes**.
The inhaled breath will sound like a crow.

2. Keep the mudra and the breath; move the hands in quick, small circles (initial movement is thumbs toward the body). The entire body should shake from the movement. After a minute or two, close your eyes and continue. **4 minutes**.

3. Interlock the fingers at the Heart Center. Jump the body off the floor. **1 minute**.

4. Bring the lock up above the head and continue jumping the buttock off the floor. **6 minutes**.
Feel like you're galloping on a horse. Do it in a rhythm. Sweat a little bit; it feels good.

Unloading the Subconscious

5. Sit with a straight spine. Interlace the fingers with the thumb tips touching. Close the eyes and concentrate on the tip of the nose. Don't let your concentration move from the tip of the nose. Inhale deep; exhale deep. Gong is played. **14 minutes**.

During the meditation, Yogi Bhajan spoke: "You are entering a reign of forgiveness. Practice forgiveness of the self. Forgive yourself. Don't fight; don't resist. You are in the region of forgiveness. This is the hemisphere of forgiveness, for your self. Redeem yourself. There is nobody above you; there is nobody beneath you; there is nobody around you; only you. This is the hemisphere where you can forgive yourself. This is a very rare opportunity. Don't ask forgiveness of God. God shall guarantee. Whatever you forgive; God shall forgive, guaranteed. Go for it! Don't fight! Forgiveness eats up the misfortune. Forgiveness eats of the misfortune of tomorrow—guaranteed. You are passing through the region of forgiveness. For the sake of giveness of God, that is what forgiveness means: for-give, for-giving. The holiness of God will open up the holes; opportunities will come. Let God give you by forgiving. Those who don't forgive get nothing."

6. With a stiff tongue and the upper palate, start repeating the sound.

Hamee Ham Tumee Tum Whaa-hay Guroo

11 minutes. Gong is played. Then the class meditated on two songs by Sat Peter Singh: *Promises*, followed by *Himalaya*.

7. Keeping the mudra, raise it above the head with the palms facing the crown of the head; stretch your arms and your spine. Breath long and deep and slow. Music is played. **2 minutes**.
TO END: Shake the arms.

Kriya to Clear Mental Paranoia

1. Sit in meditative, yogic posture. Stick out the tongue—not all the way—just relax the tongue. With the diaphragm, strongly exhale through the mouth over the relaxed tongue. This is called Paranoia Breath. This is a heavy, deep breath from the diaphragm. **1 1/2 to 3 minutes**.

Feel afraid! Do it heavily from the diaphragm. You think this is a joke. If you do it about twenty times a day you shall never have nightmares. It is not a joke—this breath. It is a yogic breath. You only do it in a natural emergency. We are asking you to do in a conscious emergency. I want it to be done by the pull of the diaphragm. When paranoia hits you, hit it with this breath.

2. Open the mouth and do Breath of Fire through a firm, rounded mouth. Breathe very quickly and forcefully. **30 seconds**.

3. Bring the hands into Ravi Mudra—ring finger and thumb together. Other three fingers are straight and open—stiff. Circle the hands around each other in front of the chest. Only the fingers move over each other—not the entire hand. Move as fast as you can. **4 minutes**.
TO END: Inhale deep, close the eyes and lock the hands at the heart center.

Your nostrils will start having pressure on ida and pingala, if you really do this exercise faster. You will have a very impulsive state here, right on the both sides where ida and pingala starts. That is all we want. Actually we want that pressure and the moment the nose starts showing a little red color in the aura. I want the big nose. They call it clown nose.

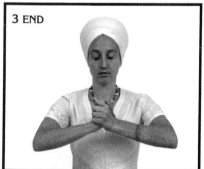

Kriya to Clear Mental Paranoia

4. Meditate with the hands gripped at the heart center. Right hand over left, grip tightly. Eyes are closed and focused at the hands. **7 minutes**.
Gong is played.

5. Relax the hands down and continue to meditate to the gong. The body will naturally adjust itself. **8 minutes**.
Music is played over the gong for the last 5 minutes. Singh Kaur's recording Beloved God is played in class. Mentally go with the sound but not the words.

6. Begin Breath of Fire. **30 seconds**. Now begin to clap the hands over the head—fast and powerful! **30 seconds**.

7. Repeat Exercise 3. **1 minute**.

8. Repeat Exercise 1: Powerful Paranoia Breath. Move the tailbone. Pull it. **1 minute**.

9. Repeat Exercise 2: Breath of Fire through rounded mouth. **15 seconds**.

10. Relax.

COMMENTS
This meditation is to jerk out the jerk in you. It is recommended to drink juice and liquids after this meditation. No solids. Also drink lots of liquids on the following day.

Clearing the Subconscious Reverse Personality

Sit in Easy Pose.

1. Bring the elbows close to the sides. Hands will naturally face toward each other. Bring the Jupiter finger and thumb together and apart, quickly opening and closing the forefinger and the thumb. Move as fast as you can. **3 1/2 minutes**.

Get stressed. Don't look at your mood, look at your strength. Doing it fast is going to be challenged by your own body, You will like to give up, the idea will come to you. You shall be transferred into a stage of duality—it's a natural tendency to either slow down or feel negative. Cut it out by personal strength—that strength is your soul, bring it out, bring the spirit out and move, really move!

Continue moving the fingers as you practice the following sounds:

    a) Whistle your National Anthem. **1 minute**.

    b) Whistle your own personal Love Call. **1 minute**.

    c) Whistle a bird call. **1 minute**.

    d) Make an animal call. Any animal of your choice. **1 minute**.

    e) Make the sound of an animal that lives in water. **1 minute**.

    f) With the lips, create the sound 'Hup'. Move the jaw. Repeat the sound very quickly. Fast! **1 minute**.

    g) Hiss like a snake. **3 minutes**.

    h) 'Cluck' the upper palate with your tongue. The tongue plays against the center of the upper palate. **1 minute**.

2. Bring the hands to the Heart Center, right hand resting on the left. Begin a powerful breath in and out through the mouth. The jaw is relaxed down and the breath moves from the diaphragm. Open the lungs. **1 minute**.

3. Keeping the hands at the heart, breathe long and deep. Close the eyes and meditate at your Heart Center. Try to feel the beat of your heart. Singing or listening, meditate on the heart. Pull the lower back in so that you can have all the flow of the serum going through the spine. Stretch out the third vertebrae. **4 1/2 minutes**.

MUSIC: *Pavan Pavan* recorded by Guru Shabd Singh.

We'll give you the power of the prana through the mantra. You can listen or you can sing if you catch these simple words. It's not difficult and there is no stress involved. But try to be with your heart, the beating instrument in you. Meditate deeply and intensely and be one with your heart. Feel your heart. Bless your heart.

Clearing the Subconscious Reverse Personality

4. Hands still at the heart, meditate on your breath. Gong is played. **12 1/2 minutes**.

Become light, hypnotically float. Mentally cut off from gravity. Physically you can't, but mentally you can.

5. Breathe a powerful Cannon Fire Breath—fast! **30 seconds**.
TO END: Inhale, suspend the breath for **15 seconds**, and move your shoulders up and down as fast as you can. Jump the shoulders. Exhale. Repeat twice more.

6. Talk to each other. Relax. **5-10 minutes**.

7. Laugh as loud as you can. You have to open your mouth, open your mouth and laugh with your tongue; that's what is required. **30 seconds**. Relax again for **2 minutes**.

COMMENTS
Yogi Bhajan suggests drinking lemon water after this set to help recuperate quickly.

Pittra Kriya

1. **Pittra Kriya**: Rest the left hand on the Heart Center and cup the right hand in front of you, with the elbow relaxed by your side. Eyes are on the tip of the nose. The right hand lifts up and passes the ear, as if you are splashing water over your shoulder. You will feel the wind pass your ear as the hand moves toward the shoulder. The wrist must cross the earlobe; the hand must travel that far back. **11 minutes**.

TO END: Inhale and suspend the breath for **15 seconds**—stretch the hand back as far as you can. Exhale. Repeat twice more.

It will hit the kidney energy. It will start working with the adrenals and then the whole system: the lungs, the central line, your hip-area, pelvic bone area. It is going to affect your body and you will become very relaxed. Do it with a rhythm and do it with a devotion and do it just to get rid of this stress. Get rid of this inner mental and physical tension. You are your vitality; minus tension, you are fine.

2. Place the elbows on the second rib below the base of the breast, in line with the nipple. Hands are slightly wider than the elbows and the palms are facing up in Shuni Mudra. The thumb covers the nail of the Saturn finger (middle finger). Eyes are at the tip of the nose. As you repeat *Har*, flick the Saturn finger. The sound *Har* is very specific and made with the tip of the tongue. The mouth remains slightly open as you generate the sound. **11 minutes**.

TO END: Inhale deeply. Continue moving the fingers. Suspend the breath for **15 seconds**. Let it open your ribcage. it will balance the chakras. Then Cannon Fire exhale. Repeat 3 times more.

You have to touch the upper palate—34, 35, 36 meridian points that relate to the hypothalamus will regulate the pituitary and take the secretion which you have created and start asking the energy to open up the chakras. It will start changing the serum of your spine. It will revitalize the gray matter in the brain.

SHUNI MUDRA

Pittra Kriya

3. Bring the arms out in front of you in a V, about 15° above shoulder height. This is Superman Pose. Hands are flat and facing down. At the rate of one repetition per second, repeat *Har* as in the second exercise, crossing the hands in front of you and keeping the arms straight. Do not bend the elbows. Alternately cross one hand over the other. Eyes focus is at the tip of the nose. **11 minutes**.

TO END: Keep moving the arms and inhale, hold for 10 seconds and Canon Breath out. Repeat 3 more times, moving the hands as fast as possible during the last repetition.

COMMENTS

There are thirty three minutes in your life, if you can spare, you can eat up your own stress. The first exercise will take care of your glandular system and will affect the liver; it will relax you. The second exercise will balance the chakras and the third exercise will balance your nervous system: parasympathetic, sympathetic.

Note: These kriyas must be done together and should never be done for less than or more than 11 minutes each.

CLEARING THE SUBCONSCIOUS
A Renewed Self-Concept

This Kriya is done in Easy Pose.

1. The left hand is on Heart Center (fingers pointing to the right). The right hand begins behind the ear with the palm facing the space behind the ear. Eyes are closed. Meditate on the tip of the nose through closed eyes. Inhale deep, exhale deep **3 times**.

The right hand comes powerfully toward the face, as if you were going to slap yourself, and just as you approach the cheek, divert the direction of the hand so that it just misses the cheek and ends up palm facing forward. **6 minutes**.

Keep a constant speed, neither too fast nor too slow. You are commanding the motor system and asking the defense mechanism to protect. It can give you a powerful immune system. Understand that everything in you is controlled by the brain. All glandular secretion is also commanded by the brain. Glands are the guardians of health and we need those juices to get to the next stage.

2. Eyes are focused at the tip of the nose. Gather the hands together in front of the chest, as if cupping water, and then bring the hands up to the throat and extend the arms, as though pouring the water from the tips of your fingers. **15 minutes**.

Fill up all your anger, attachments, and resentment in your hands, anything that is bothering you, and then let it go. Pull out all the pain of the subconscious, and fill the hands with it and offer it to the space. From day 1 to the 11th year, all the pains of your childhood, day-by-day, month-by-month, year-by-year, bring it up and give it to the space.

3. Bring the hands in front of the face and look at the lines of your hand. Study your own hand. **5 minutes**.

A Renewed Self-Concept

4. Cover the face and eyes with the hands. Try to see into infinity through your closed eyes. **15 minutes**.

5. Hands cross at the Heart Center, right hand over the left. Inhale deep and hold. Exhale. **3 times**. Chant: ***Har Haray Haree Whaa-Hay Guroo.*** **5 minutes**. Then, whisper strongly for **30 seconds**.
Create a systematic sound. Pause between each syllable of the mantra. Done in a monotone without music. Addresses the tattvas and the aura.

6. Bend forward and place your hands on the ground. You may come into Baby Pose if you prefer. Anahata Choir version of *Ardas Bhaee* is played. Yogi Bhajan plays the gong lightly & intermittently over the recording. **11 minutes**. TO END: Stretch your hands forward as hard as you can and come up. Keep your eyes closed.

7. Stretch the arms above the head in Prayer Pose. Absolute prayer. Create your own profile in prayer now. State your intention; who you want to be. Make a profile. Not a prayer—profile in prayer. This is what you want to be. **3 minutes**.

8. Shake your hands vigorously. Shake your whole body. **30 seconds to 1 minute**. Sit and relax.

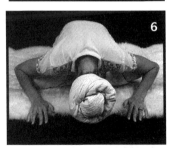

9. Wave your hands in front of your face and eyes to clear your eyesight. Just a few seconds.

TO END: Close the eyes and inhale deeply. Take this prana into every part of your body. Let the breath of life circulate. Exhale. Inhale deep. Hold it tight. Circulate it throughout your entire being. Exhale. Inhale deep. Suspend. Feel the pranic energy from the tip of your hair to your toes. (Gong is played lightly.) Exhale.

COMMENTS
Yogi Bhajan suggested taking vitamin C to prepare for this meditation.

Break the Mask

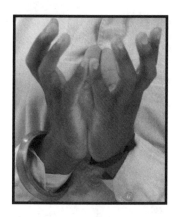

Sit in Easy Pose with a straight spine.

MUDRA: The heels of the hands are together in front of the heart center in an open lotus. The sides of the thumb tips meet, as do the sides of the little fingers. All the fingers are open and spread but are not stiffly held. It looks like an open flower. The fingers point upward.

EYES: 1/10th open, or as you like.

MANTRA: Chant the following mantra in a steady pace and in a tune you like that preserves its beat.

Har Jee Har Har Har Har Har Jee

BREATH: Chant the mantra mentally with the following Segmented Breath:
  Inhale one-third of the way and hold for 15 seconds.
  Inhale another one-third and hold 15 seconds.
  Inhale completely and suspend for a final 15 seconds, then exhale.

1. Continue for 15 minutes. (With practice, this sequence of inhaling and suspending the breath can be taken up to a One Minute Breath: three 20 second holds.)

2. Chant the mantra aloud for **11 minutes**.

3. Repeat exercise 1 for **5 more minutes**.

TOTAL TIME: **31 minutes**.

COMMENTS

The mantra means *"O, my soul, (the creative) God is, God is, God is, God is, O, my soul."* *Har* manifests from the Infinite subtlety of God into immediate experience. The double form—the palindromic sequence of sounds—manifests the state of creative Infinity itself. It opens your soul to be real and your mind to link effectively to your real identity. In the mudra, the thumbs connect to represent *"I am"* and the little fingers *"I shall be."* The three fingers that are open represent the past, present and future. So between how you are and how your soul will bloom, all of time serves you. It is a mudra for your connection and flow of life from your essence; its subtle and electromagnetic form adjusts the projection of the heart center and lets your words go deeply into your mind to guide your new behaviors.

Meditation to Remove Inner Conflicts

Sit straight in Easy Pose.

MUDRA: Interlock the fingers in Venus Lock (with the thumbs interlocked and the hands forming a cupped position) in front of the solar plexus.

EYES: Eyes are closed.

MANTRA: Chant, listen and understand the mantra:

Hamee Ham Brahm Ham *(We are we, we are God)*

The recording by Nirinjan Kaur *(Humee Hum)* was used in this class.

TIME: **11-22 minutes**.
This was taught for 22 minutes. Best to begin with 11 minutes and build up to 22 minutes.

END: Inhale deeply and hold. Asses yourself while holding the breath. Exhale. Repeat 2 more times. Relax.

COMMENTS

This meditation was given to create the power of effective communication.
After doing the above meditation, meditate for a few minutes and continue to assess yourself:
   Did you hear what you were saying?
   Could you hear and understand exactly what you were saying?
   Are your words entering your heart as real and precious so you will stand behind what you create? If not it takes away all energy and reality. Confirm and establish your communication to be conscious, direct and real.

Meditation for the Negative Mind

Sit straight in Easy Pose.

MUDRA: Make a cup of the two hands with both palms facing up, and the right hand resting on top of the left hand. The fingers will cross over each other. Put this open cup at the level of the heart center. Elbows are relaxed at the sides.

EYES: Your eyes are slightly open and look down toward the hands.

BREATH & FOCUS: Inhale deeply in a long steady stroke through the nose. Exhale in a focused stream through rounded lips. You will feel the breath go over the hands. Let any thought or desire that is negative, or persistently distracting come into your mind as you breathe. Breathe the thought and feeling in, and exhale it out with the breath.

TIME: **11 to 31 minutes**.

TO END: Exhale completely and suspend the breath out as you lock in the Navel Point. Concentrate on each vertebra of the spine until you can feel it all the way to the base, as stiff as a rod. Then inhale powerfully, exhale completely, and repeat the concentration. Repeat this final breath **3-5 times**. Then relax completely.

COMMENTS
When you need to balance the flashing negativity and protective fervor of the Negative Mind, use this meditation. It clears the subconscious of unwanted negative or fearful thoughts. Then the Negative Mind can give you clear signals to protect and to promote you. The posture is one of calmness and humility that lets the Creator, the Unknown, cover and shield you. Traditionally, this posture was known as Beggar's Bowl.

Guru Gaitree Mantra Meditation

Sit straight in Easy Pose.

MUDRA: Hands on knees in Gyan Mudra.

EYES: Focus at the brow point.

MANTRA: Chant this mantra on one breath. It takes about 15 seconds:

Gobinday	*Sustains You*
Mukanday	*Liberates You*
Udaaray	*Elevates You*
Apaaray	*Delivers You Across*
Hareeang	*Destroys All*
Kareeang	*Creates All*
Nirnaamay	*Beyond Category and Name*
Akaamay	*Beyond Desire*

To chant it correctly, inhale deeply, pull in the navel, and apply Mulbandh as you begin to chant. Pull the Mulbandh a little tighter with each phrase. Exhale and continue.

TIME: Chant for **31 minutes**.

COMMENTS

This meditation works on subconscious blocks, especially around issues of fear. It is a Core Alignment Meditation for the Defender Aspect of the mind. This Aspect looks at everything based on how it may affect you. "How will it hurt me or direct me away from what I am trying to do?" It defends. It is a practical sequence-oriented mental pattern. It wants to know how to deal with it now. What is the action needed? Is it a personal threat, directed at you, or an accident with errors you can correct, or a pure act of nature and coincidence? When the Negative Mind is too strong, you may appear to be rigid, reactive, and over-dominant. When balanced you deliver strong focused actions and you enjoy challenge. You act, but always with a cover and a back-up plan.

CHAPTER SEVEN

RENEWING
THE BRAIN

MASTERING THE SELF

Changing Gears

Our fundamental right as human beings is to live our destiny—to be healthy, happy and holy. The way we express that right is by rewriting the patterns in our brains; that is, literally, rewiring our responses to life so that we can quit reacting and begin living. Our brains are the most sophisticated, responsive, elastic mechanisms in the Universe. Although our intellectual capacity peaks early, age 22, our capacity to change grows as we exercise it. The mind is our intention, our identity, our purpose; the brain is what we use to fulfill it. This capacity to fulfill our intention, our word, is blocked by old patterns, old habits and old responses. Hence, the capacity to rewire the brain is an essential human asset. Neuroplasticity describes the brains ability to create new neural networks, adapt old ones, and respond with a new pattern. Stroke victims learn to speak and walk again; they re-learn fine motor skills. How? They create new neural networks, new patterns in the brain that adapt and learn. The part of the brain that used to speak and understand language is now dead, so the brain adapts and co-opts nontraditional language centers of the brain in order to learn to speak and write again. This is neuroplasticity; this is flexibility; this is our human capacity.

As yogis, we use the eyes—*drishti*; and the hands—*mudras*; and the tongue—*mantra*; to rewire our brains. On the subtle level, we move and arrange the tattvas in new patterns so that our brain can rewire itself. We drop the past and begin to respond in new ways; we invite new experiences in as we let go of old habits. This is the true discipline of the law of attraction. Change your Self so that you change what you invite in.

"When you are at the same frequency with the cosmic energy, opportunities come to you, when you are at a different frequency then opportunities may be there, but you cannot feel them, know them, or act upon them, therefore they don't exist for you."
–Yogi Bhajan, April 11, 1976

The Frontal Lobe is the seat of the human experience—our personality, our reason, our judgment; the capacity to respond instead of react. Developing a mature, responsive, frontal lobe can mean the difference between irrational, erratic behaviors and sophisticated, skilled responses. The Golden Chord, between the pituitary and the pineal, is activated by the eyes and the stimulation of the hypothalamus. The seat of the Third Eye, the frontal lobe, intuits, discerns and directs us to act. These kriyas for the frontal lobe create a heaviness in the forehead and Brow Point, challenging the hypothalamus and pituitary to respond effectively.

The Brain Doctor stimulates the entire brain and awakens higher functioning in all the glands through increased circulation and challenge. The exercises in Balance the Mind I & II connote the importance of movement and relaxation in order to be effective mentally and emotionally. The final two kriyas in this chapter, Anti-Depression and Brain Synchrony and Mental Exercises, use mudra to bring the brain into balance, balancing the glandular secretions throughout both hemispheres of the brain and throughout the body.

Renewing the brain is your fundamental human right to manifest your own destiny and live a life of purpose. These kriyas help you rewrite your patterns and rewire your circuits, so that you can live as a free man, a free woman, a free spirit.

"I know the science to refresh the neurons in the brain and throughout all seven layers of the individual (the chakras). And with all that knowledge, and being a yogi, and using all the supernatural powers that go with it, I still found that there is one very simple way to be happy. All that knowledge brought me to conclude one small thing—and it is three words: Sadhana, Aradhana, and Prabhupathi. If you study the whole truth of the universe; if you find God in your presence, sitting on the opposite chair having lunch with you, still you will be empty. You have to learn only one thing: this universe is a magnetic field, and under this Earth is a magnet. The stationary

Sun flares and the Moon wanes and waxes; there are seven main stars that affect you: Jupiter, Saturn, Sun, Mercury, your Id, Mars, and the Moon. There are mounds and antennas for each of these in your very hand. This is how the energy affects you. . . .

"This Infinite energy of God, this Infinite psyche of creativity, has to be transformed in you. If it comes too directly, it will space you out. You will be useless. If it's not there, you will be miserable. But if it's coming properly, and you can change the gears as needed, it will be fantastic! There are three words: Sadhana, Aradhana, and Prabhupati. It will give you mastery of God's Word."

–Yogi Bhajan, May 9, 1992

The Brain Doctor

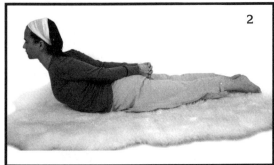

1. Sit in Lotus Pose. Place the hands by the hips and bounce up and down using the hands to push the body up off the floor. Move rapidly in coordination with Breath of Fire for **2 minutes**.

To the Yogi, one's own age is measured by flexibility. When a man cannot sit in Lotus Pose he is equivalent to 40 years of age and when a woman cannot sit in Lotus Pose, she is equivalent to 120 years of age.

2. Lie on the stomach with the forehead on the floor. Interlock the hands at the small of the back. Inhale and raise the head and upper torso as high as possible then exhale down to the original position. Repeat the cycle **52 times**.

This exercise helps adjust the ribcage.

3. As in Exercise 2, inhale and raise the head and upper torso as high as possible, and at the same time strike the buttocks with both heels. Exhale and relax down. Repeat this cycle **52 times**, then relax with the arms by the sides.

This exercise strengthens the lower back and helps eliminate lower back pain.

4. Lie on the back with the fingers interlaced at the Navel Point. Jump the legs up and back toward the head, lifting the buttocks off the ground. Repeat this jumping motion **52 times**.

This exercise is great for releasing pent-up tension and frustration!

5. Squat into Crow Pose. Extend the arms straight in front parallel to the ground with the palms together.
   a) Inhale, stand up and clap the hands over the head
   b) Exhale, squat down and clap the hands straight in front.
Repeat the complete cycle **52 times**.

The Brain Doctor

6. This is a four-part exercise. Each part is done for four counts.

a) Begin by sitting in Easy Pose with the arms extended to the sides, parallel to the ground, palms facing down. Keep the arms perfectly straight and tight like iron throughout the following sequence.

b) First pump the arms **3 times** as though you were flying. On the fourth count, firmly slap the ground with the hands.

c) Second, pump the arms **3 times** and on the fourth count clap the hands above the head.

d) Third, pump the arms **3 times**. On the fourth count extend the arms in front parallel to the ground and clap the hands.

e) Finally, pump the arms **3 times** and on the fourth count clap the hands behind the head.

When the sequence becomes familiar, substitute the mantra *Har Har Har Haree* for the counting. Chant in rhythm with the movement for **2 minutes**.

This sequence focuses on the brain. Using the mantra Har Har Har Hari causes the projective brain to assist the initial brain. Keeping the arms straight and tight stimulates reflexology points along the arms and "is better than the best acupuncture."

continued on next page

The Brain Doctor

7. Repeat the entire series of postures in exercise 6 using the Guru Gaitree Mantra:

Gobinday, Mukanday, Udaaray, Apaaray,
Hareeang, Kareeang, Nirnaamay, Akaamay

The sequence is the same but the pumping motion is faster. Pump the arms up and down once with each word of the mantra. Clap the hands on **Apaaray** and **Akaamay**. Continue for **3 minutes**.

Using the Guru Gaitree Mantra is more difficult because there are more words to match with the actions. The eastern zone, or the initial and projective part of the brain, is stimulated by the word difference in the mantra. The Guru Gaitree Mantra is unique in its ability to effectively balance the initial and projective brain. When both parts of the brain unite in a balanced way, it enables the brain to function creatively, to communicate effectively and project any necessary defense. This exercise tests your I.Q.

8. Repeat Exercise 6 for **3 minutes**.

9. Sit in Easy Pose with the eyes closed and meditate on the song, *Himalaya* or another beautiful song. As you listen, let the sound of the words and music create a frequency for the right brain to receive and then stimulate the left-brain to create movement. Sing along with the tape and imagine you are flying at 40 thousand feet. Meditatively move the shoulders, torso, arms and hands to creatively express yourself. This is a basic human movement. Express your feelings freely through your body movement for **5 minutes**.

You can develop great healing power in your hands by learning to project beautiful songs in this way. It is an effective means of communicating with your inner self and projecting your essence outward. That essence is the healing force within you, which is God. It is especially beneficial for a woman to develop the ability to express herself through her body language to effectively communicate her presence. Otherwise, she taxes her sensual, sexual and sensitive self and loses her balance.

COMMENTS

Effective communication is when you can communicate the total you, honestly and freely. The two hemispheres of the brain must be in synchronized relationship for this to happen. This kriya is a brain doctor. It patches the two hemispheres together so you can both sense and project who you really are. This series reduces overall body tension and enhances the awareness of the self. The inner creative self can project its essence outward. Equally, it can receive the wholeness of others with complete empathy and intuition.

Kriya for the Frontal Lobe

1. Sit in Easy Pose with your hands on your knees. The chest is out and the shoulders are back. Maintaining this posture, begin vibrating the front of the face, using a very rapid and short up–and–down motion. Try to move just the forehead. The breath will adjust itself. Continue for **8-9 minutes**.

This exercise is called Mastak Subhaee. It works on the change and replacement of gray matter in the brain.

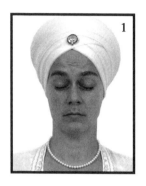

2. Remain in Easy Pose with the hands on the knees. Begin rolling the head on the neck in the shape of a figure eight. The chin comes down to the center of the chest with each circle, twice in a full repetition of the movement. Make sure that the exercise is performed powerfully and steadily with equal timing for each revolution of the head. Continue for **3 minutes** at a moderate pace and then sit still for **30 seconds**.

This exercise is called Infinity Kriya. It is very powerful and must be done carefully and consciously. The effect is to balance the central ear, which affects clear and conscious thought.

3. Still in Easy Pose, bring the arms straight out from the sides of the body palms up at shoulder level. Bring the hands into fists with the thumbs outside. Inhale and bring both fists in to the top of the shoulders while stretching the elbows out as powerfully as possible and flexing your biceps. Return to the original position on the exhale. Continue the motion for **9 minutes**.

Recording of Sukhmanee Sahib is played.

4. Remain in Easy Pose. Still listening to *Sukhmanee Sahib*, stretch the arms straight out in front of the body at a 45-degree angle with the palms facing down, fingers held together on each hand. In this position begin shaking the head as fast as possible in a very short sideways motion. Shake the skull in a continuous motion for **1 minute**. Inhale and relax.

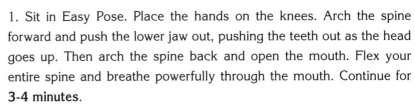

Kriya for the Frontal Brain

1. Sit in Easy Pose. Place the hands on the knees. Arch the spine forward and push the lower jaw out, pushing the teeth out as the head goes up. Then arch the spine back and open the mouth. Flex your entire spine and breathe powerfully through the mouth. Continue for **3-4 minutes**.

This exercise works on the frontal brain.

2. Sit in Crow Pose, a squatting position with the feet flat on the floor, knees apart. Place the hands on the waist. Stand up while inhaling through the mouth, pushing the lower jaw forward, pushing the teeth out. Then exhale through the open mouth as you lower yourself back down into Crow Pose. Continue for **2-3 minutes**.

This exercise works on the meridian points in the thigh, which are connected with sexual energy and compassion. The thigh bone controls the balance of potassium and calcium, and the inflow and outflow of energy.

3. Sit down in Easy Pose with the forearms bent up at the sides, hands at face level. The palms face out, away from each other.

    a) Bring the right forearm out, straightening the arm so that it is parallel to the ground, palm down. Then return to the original position and repeat with the left arm.

    b) Continue alternating arms fast and hard for **6 minutes**.

This exercise pressurizes the frontal brain at the Third Eye Point.

4. a) Remain in Easy Pose, with hands above the shoulders in fists, thumbs locked inside pressing the mound of the little finger. This is the original position. The movements are in a 4-count rhythm as follows:

    b) Bring right arm out and up 60°. Return to original position.

    c) Bring left arm out and up 60°. Return to original position.

    d) Bring both arms straight up over head, parallel to each other. Return them to original position. Continue this rhythm moving fast and powerfully for **6-7 minutes**.

Kriya for the Frontal Brain

5. Still in Easy Pose, stretch the arms straight out in front, parallel to the ground with the palms facing up. Bend the middle (Saturn) fingers into the palms and lock your thumbs over them. The other fingers are straight. Moving the arms together, pump them up and down, moving about 12 inches above and 12 inches below the original position. The breath will come naturally in rhythm with the motion. Keep the elbows straight and move fast and powerfully for **3 minutes**.

This exercise works on breaking up deposits in the neck that block circulation to the brain. It also works on patience, the quality of the Saturn finger.

6. Come into Frog Pose, squatting down so the buttocks are resting on the heels, which are off the ground and touching each other. The fingertips are on the ground between the knees, and the head is up. Inhale and raise the buttocks high, keeping the fingertips on the ground and the heels up. Exhale and come down to the starting position, letting the buttocks strike the heels. Breathe deeply and powerfully as you move, and continue until you have done **54 cycles**, approximately **2-3 minutes**.

7. Come into Rock Pose, sitting on the heels with the tops of the feet on the ground. In this position, repeat the arm movements of exercise 4. Continue for **2 minutes**.

This works on the digestion and the removal of deposits and toxins in the breast area.

8. Stand up, close your eyes and dance, moving every muscle of the entire body without moving far from your original spot. Flow with the rhythm, mirroring the notes and words with body language. The music used in class was Don Cooper's *Twelve Months*. Continue **25 minutes**.

This is called natural dancing instinct. It gives the body a chance to release deposited toxins. Effective communication uses body language to express and project the words we speak. Those who do not express their psyche through the vibration of the body will fail in communication and action.

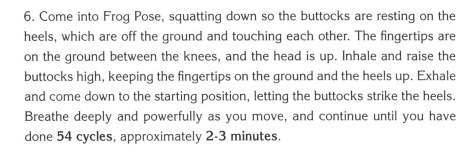
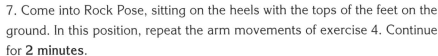

Balance the Mind I

1. Sit in Easy Pose. Hands are locked in front of the heart center, palm to palm, the four fingers folded around the opposite hand. Look at the tip of the nose. Squeeze the hands. **3 1/2 minutes**. Synchronize the entire body.
   Squeeze the entire body as tightly as you squeeze the hands. **3 1/2 minutes**.
Squeeze like you are squeezing water out of a stone. You will find an air vacuum in your palms. It will give you sensitivity of how life flows. Experience it. Squeeze the hands with maximum tightness. Look at the tip of nose, concentrate, and squeeze. You will breathe differently, exist differently, and start to eliminate disease from your body. By fixing the optical nerve—bifocally to zero angle—the pineal and the pituitary come to one obedience.

2. Immediately lie down on the back. Bring the arms and legs up to 90°— straight and tight. Palms are facing the knees. Spread the fingers wide. **2 minutes**.

3. Bring the knees to the chest and wrap your arms around the knees. Bring the nose to the knees. Don't cross the feet. Stabilize. **3 1/2 minutes**.

4. Come into Corpse Pose and let the body relax. Kulwant Singh's recording of *Chattr Chakkr Varti* is played. **1 minute**.
Nap. Hypnotically sleep. Conquer the environments. Don't let the body move but imagine you are out of your body, let your soul look at it, and dance.

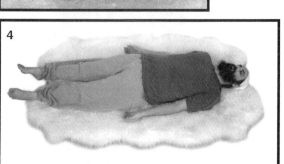

Balance the Mind I

5. Cat stretch to each side and transition to standing. **30 seconds**.

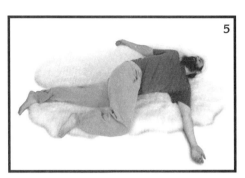

6. Dance with hands up above the shoulders. Keep the hands up the entire time. *Chattr Chakkr Varti* continues playing for **2 1/2 minutes**. *Rhythms of Gatka* is played for the remainder of the dance. Keep only one foot on the ground at a time. Dance vigorously. **11 minutes total**.

Open the hips, shake the rib cage, tighten and loosen the neck, the face. Every part of the body has to dance. Eight twists of the body in one beat. Raise the Kundalini. Infinite healing can take place. This is an Ashta—eight—beat rhythm, an Ashtang Natiem. It is called Shiva Dance.

7. Relax and sit down. **3 1/2 minutes**.

8. Massage the armpits deeply; each hand massaging the opposite armpit concurrently. **1 1/2 minutes**.

This will stimulate the three nervous systems and give you a new life.

9. Beat the upper part of your chest with your fists. **30 seconds**. Then beat the thighs just above the knee. Fast and heavy. It has a soothing effect. **30 seconds**.

Balance the Mind II

1. Lie down on your back. Bring your arms and legs up to 90 degrees. Toes point toward the ceiling. Spread the fingers wide, palms facing the thighs. After **3 minutes** begin singing loudly, from the navel, to the *Aquarian March* by Nirinjan Kaur. Continue for **7 minutes**.

Let the energy come in and take care of the lower back. If your knees bend it means you worry too much. This posture is between headstand and shoulder stand and gives you a new brain, new pelvis, and takes care of the liver.

2. Immediately bring your knees to your chest and wrap your arms around the knees. Press very firmly. Bring your nose up to your knees. Do not let your feet cross. Continue chanting powerfully with the *Aquarian March*. **5 1/2 minutes**.

Pressing the knees to the chest will open the 2nd and 3rd lumbar vertebrae.

3. Shiva Dance. Stand up immediately and dance with hands above the head and shoulders. Fingers towards the ceiling. Allow only one foot to be on the ground at a time. *Rhythms of Gatka* recording is played. **15 minutes**.

You must have 8 movements, 8 curls in your body per beat; it is called Ashtang Natiem. It is a Temple Dance. You must not lower the hands; if you do so it neutralizes the energy—reversing the effect. Heal yourself.

Balance the Mind II

4. Immediately come sitting on your heels.

4a,b,c

a) Dance with the arms. **1 1/2 minutes**.
This will heal the stomach and it will hurt because you've been eating junk.

b) Continue dancing with the hands over your head and move the rib cage. **1 minute**.
This will get rid of disease.

c) Now begin moving freely, dance vigorously and fast with the beat. Move the whole body. **1 minute**.
This will give you perfect healing and energize the body.

d) Now begin clapping the hands. Do it hard and pressure the fingers. **1 minute**.
This will help to get rid of arthritis.

e) Beat the chest very fast and hard with your fists. **1 minute**.

4e

TO END: Inhale deep and hold. Exhale. Repeat twice more—letting the breath grow deeper with each consecutive breath. Twist the body slowly to the left and then to the right. Relax for a few minutes before moving to the next posture.

5. Easy Pose. Sit solid and contained. Bring the hands to Prayer Pose at the heart center—apply equal pressure in both hands. Keep this pressure in the hands. Eyes at the tip of the nose. Sing with the *Say Saraswati* recording by Nirinjan Kaur. **8 minutes**.

TO END: Inhale deep. Hold for **15 seconds**. Exhale cannon breath. Repeat twice more.

This will crown the entire kriya. You are getting the entire universe in you—all powers—nine special powers, eighteen occult powers, total knowledge, total power, total prosperity, all the three universes, freedom from death, power to uplift and serve, victory over cause and effect, infinite to the infinity of God, all transparent and nontransparent powers shall serve thee.

5

Mental Exercises

Sit in Easy Pose with a straight spine.

MANTRA: Chanting to *Rakhe Rakhanhar*, you will move through a series of eight postures, one posture for each line of the mantra.

TIME: **1 hour 45 minutes**.

Rakhay rakhanhaar aap ubaarian

Bend the elbow, raise the right hand with palm inward at face level, midway between side and front. Keep the head forward, look into the hand as if it were a mirror, shifting the eyes to the right so you are looking out of the corner of your eyes. *This works on the optical nerve.*

Gur kee pairee paa-eh kaaj savaarian

Bring both hands to the brow line with palms down, as if shading eyes. Gaze far away.
Lets you see into the future.

Hoaa aap dayaal manho na visaarian

Rest the right elbow on the thigh and let the forehead rest on the right hand.
This is confirmation.

Saadh janaa kai sang bhavjal taarian

Bring hands to either side of the head at face level and make the hands into claws with palms forward. Lock the back teeth and squint the eyes.
Gives you grit. It is the inner wake-up.

Mental Exercises

Saakat nindak dusht khin maa-eh bidaarian
Turn to the left, rest the left elbow on the thigh. Rest the chin in the fingers of the left hand, with the thumb pressing underneath the chin and side of the index finger pressing below mouth. Raise and lower eyes twice, gazing off. *This is the Philosopher.*

Tis saahib kee tayk naanak manai maa-eh
Slap the cheeks with both hands simultaneously, eyes closed. Without fear.
Works on parasympathetic nervous system.
This is Absolution.

Jis simrat sukh ho-eh saglay dookh jaa-eh
Cross arms on the chest, arch spine, cock head back and tilt to the right. Smile.
This will give feeling of reality and adversity. This is "Macho."

Jis simrat sukh ho-eh saglay dookh jaa-eh
Arms open wide to 45 degrees.
This is "Welcoming God."

Anti-Depression & Brain Synchrony

1. Sit in Easy Pose with an erect spine. The hands are in Gyan Mudra with the first finger and thumb touching.

a) Raise the upper arms parallel to the ground and bring the mudra in front of the eyes so that the thumbs and forefingers of each hand touch in front of the bridge of the nose. Open the eyes wide and stare beyond the hands to the horizon.

b) Inhale deeply and separate the hands 36-45 inches while keeping the eyes fixed. Exhale and return to the original position. The elbows will move a little, but keep them relaxed.

Start with a slow movement, one cycle of the breath taking about 4 seconds. As the hands go outward with the inhale, mentally vibrate *Saa*. As they return, vibrate *Taa*. Then, for the second repetition, mentally vibrate *Naa* on the inhale and *Maa* on the exhale. Meditate on the life energy of the breath.The feeling of stretching the breath from a single point, represented by the meeting of the mudras, outward to the full extension of the mudras is essential. After 2 to 3 minutes, increase the speed to 3 to 4 seconds for each cycle of *Saa-Taa-Naa-Maa*. Continue for **3 minutes**.

2. Inhale and relax with the arms and shoulders totally surrendered down. No mudra is needed, just relax. Meditate at the Crown Chakra at the top of the head. If you must concentrate at all, focus all your energy at the anterior fontanel, on top of the skull. Place all of your concentration on totally relaxing or on that one square inch of the skull. Continue for about **15 minutes**.

TIME: You can increase the time of the meditation and relaxation slowly over a period of weeks. Ultimately you can do Exercise 1 for **11 minutes** followed by Exercise 2 for **31 minutes**.

COMMENTS

You are born and made to be positive and creative. The creativity of your existence is unlimited. Because we do not have the established habit of constancy in thought and action, we create negative patterns in our thoughts and actions; we generate our own depressions. This meditation will let you evaluate and measure how positive or negative you are. It will also make you positive and happy. It focuses on the range of the breath. In the subconscious, breath and life are synonymous. By meditating this way, depression can be alleviated. If you do it correctly, there will be a tremendous pressure at your lymph glands. The two sides of the brain get coordinated and separated. Those unfortunate people who used marijuana at any time in their life get the hemispheres confused. The effect is periodic scatteredness, lack of motivation, depression or alienation. This can recur anytime throughout the lifespan, even after years of abstinence from drug use. The body needs to be readjusted through an appropriate beet fast and banana fast. This exercise will also help to coordinate the brain functions.

CHAPTER EIGHT

VITALITY

MASTERING THE SELF

Building Stamina & Strength

*"Leadership is the law of the Age of Aquarius; rhythm
is the law of happiness; and love is the law of victory."*
–Yogi Bhajan

Vitality is the key to not only surviving but thriving in the Aquarian Age. As yogis, we have the tools to energize, balance and strengthen our nervous and glandular systems so that we can respond to life with consciousness—not react to life from fear. Vitality depends on a strong Navel Point; the ability to absorb and use prana, in your breath, your food and your environments; efficient metabolism, digestion and elimination; a strong and flexible spine; and the capacity to relax and restore.

Our culture would have us believe that vitality is essentially a quality of youth, something that can be regained with a pill or a diet or an exercise regimen. Instead, vitality is a state of consciousness. Vitality is an ease and flexibility found in our bodies and a strength found in our will. Vitality is a state of optimal performance: body, mind and soul. Vitality can be found in surrender—Bhakti. When we align our will with the Infinite, then we have access to the power of the Infinite—Shakti—and dwell in the flow of life.

As we transition to the Aquarian Age, the ability to surrender to the flow will make or break our capacity to respond effectively; because the pressures will only continue to increase. We all need to be as vital as we can possibly be in order to serve and uplift ourselves and everyone around us. Vitality doesn't mean just energy; it also means a moral and ethical integrity that guides our identity and our decision-making; a flexibility and tolerance that not only allows for differences but also forgives shortcomings; and a capacity for change that embraces the future with hope instead of succumbing to doubt or fear.

"Time is going to be rough whether you like it or not. Time will force you to adjust and change. Let us see how powerful your mind can be, what vastness you can achieve. You have to let the stress go through self-hypnosis. You have to intuitively know what will lead to what. You have to learn, without seeing auras, what is in-between the lines. You have to understand: leadership is the law of the Age of Aquarius; rhythm is the law of happiness; and love is the law of victory. Just remember these three things and you will not be upset. Love is a power, it gives; leadership is an excellence, it makes your entire nervous system excellent because you don't want to be wrong. Life is a challenge, face it. You have the capacity, inside, that can put you on the stars—and that is your mind."

–Yogi Bhajan, September 10, 1992

This chapter opens with kriyas that build our aerobic capacity, strengthen the navel and stimulate the metabolic system. Kriya to Become Super Human stimulates both sides of the brain as well as the Navel Point. Inner Vitality & Stamina stimulates the glandular system while Kriya to Take Away Stress helps facilitate relaxation by stimulating the lower triangle and building the arcline. Sanmukh Kriya builds courage and Boundless Strength rejuvenates the spine. And the final two kriyas address issues specifically related to strengthening a man's capacity to endure and a woman's need for relaxation from stress.

Every kriya and meditation included in this chapter builds stamina, courage and strength, physically, mentally and spiritually so that you can meet the challenges of the new Age with face and grace—and vitality!

Har Aerobic Kriya

1. Standing with feet comfortably apart, clap the hands over the head **8 times**. Each time you clap, chant *HAR* with the tip of the tongue.

2. Bend over from the hips. Slap the ground hard with the hands 8 times. With each pat, chant *HAR* with the tip of the tongue.

3. Stand up straight up with arms out to the sides parallel to the ground. Raise and lower the arms, patting the air, one foot up and one foot below the shoulder height, as you chant *HAR* with the tip of the tongue. **8 times**.

4. Still standing, jump and crisscross the arms and legs chanting *HAR*, both as the arms and legs cross, and when they are out at the sides, for a total of **8 chants** of *HAR*.

Har Aerobic Kriya

5. Come into Archer Pose with the right leg forward, left leg back. Bend the right knee, extending in and out of the full stretch of the position, chanting *HAR* each time you bend forward. **8 times.** Switch sides, with the left leg extended forward, chanting *HAR* each time you bend forward. **8 times.**

6. Repeat crisscross jumping as in Exercise 4.

7. Stretch the arms over the head. Arch the back as you bend backwards, chanting *HAR* each time you bend back. **8 times.**

8. Repeat crisscross jumping as in Exercise 4.

9. With the arms straight up over the head, bend to the left **4 times** and bend to the right **4 times**, chanting *HAR* each time you bend. Keep the arms close to the head.

COMMENTS

This set is to be done very quickly, moving from exercise to exercise with no break. When done properly it is a great aerobic workout. Repeat the sequence 5 times. The mantra *HAR* means Creative Infinity.

Advanced Abdominal & Navel Strengthening

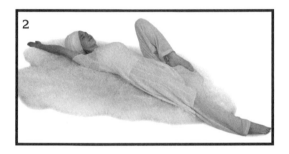

1. Alternate Leg Lifts. Come lying down flat on the back. Have the arms by the sides with the palms down. Have the hands underneath the buttocks if needed. Inhale and lift the left leg up to a 90° angle to the floor with the toe pointed to the ceiling. Exhale as you lower the leg down. Inhale and lift the right leg up to a 90° angle to the floor with the toe pointed to the ceiling. Exhale and lower the leg down. Long Slow Deep Breathing. 1-**3 minutes**.

2. Cross Crawl. Remain lying down flat on the back with the arms by the sides, palms flat against the floor. On the inhale, bring the left knee up to the chest and at the same time bring the right arm onto the ground down back and behind you in a kind of straight arm backstroke motion. Exhale yourself flat. Inhale with opposite arm and opposite leg. Continue, inhaling through the nose and exhaling through the nose concentrating the breath's energy at the Navel Point. 1-**3 minutes**.

3. Triangle Pose. Draw the knees up to the chest and rock yourself up. Slowly come standing up. Bring the feet approximately shoulder width apart, the feet creating a right angle to the plane of the body. Bend from the waist and place the hands on the floor. Hands are narrower than shoulder width apart. Have the thumb tips touching if possible. Elbows and knees are straight and the head is in line with the upper arms. Tilt the pelvis forward and push down through the shoulders, keeping equal weight on the hands and feet. Hold the position. Long Slow Deep Breathing. 1-**3 minutes**.

4.Cobra Pose. Come lying down flat on the stomach. Bring the chin on the ground with the palms down on the floor underneath and slightly forward of the shoulders. Have the legs together, tops of the feet on the ground. Inhale and raise the head up, chest up and now smoothly push yourself up. Make sure the arms are shoulder width apart, elbows a little bent, fingers pointing forward, shoulders rolled back and down, chest high and head back. The whole pelvic area is on the ground. You can be resting on the forearms, if it is more comfortable for you. Hold the position. Long Slow Deep Breathing. **1-3 minutes**.

Advanced Abdominal & Navel Strengthening

5. Yoga Crunch. Roll back over on the back. Bring knees up and have your feet flat against the floor. Make the hands into a basket by interlacing them and placing them behind the head. We are going to doing a six-count movement both up and down. Lift the head off the ground and remember to just support the head with the hands; do not pull with the hands or arms. Tilt the pelvis so that the lower back is flat against the floor. Keep the lower back flat throughout the exercise. In this position, inhale slowly, exhale and slowly curl up tightening the abdominal muscles. One...two... three... four... five... six. Now inhale and slowly loosen the abdominal as you go back. One...two...three...four...five...six. Keep the head up in both positions. This will help you keep the lower back flat against the floor. Continue, go slow and concentrate your energy right at your navel point. Imagine you are breathing in and out through the navel. This will help you concentrate on this area of the body. **1-3 minutes**.

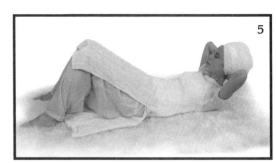

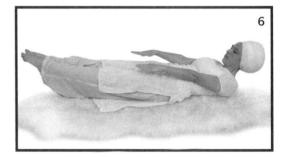

6. Stretch Pose. Lie flat on the back. Lift the upper back and shoulders off the ground, keeping the lower back flat against the surface. Bring the arms up over the trunk of the body with the hands about shoulder width apart. Lift the legs up with toes pointed away from the body and level with the eyes. Keep the heels lightly resting on the ground, if needed. Breath of Fire. 1-**3 minutes**.

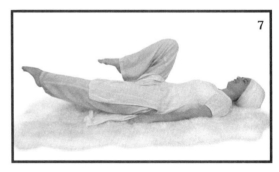

7. Leg Thrusts. Remain lying on the back. Bring both knees to the chest. Have the arms by the sides with the palms down. Place the hands underneath the buttocks if needed. Inhale and thrust the left leg out so it is about 12 inches off the ground with the toe pointed away from the body. Exhale and switch legs. Use Powerful Deep Breaths. **1-3 minutes**.

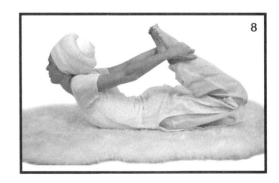

8. Bow Pose. Roll over on to the stomach. Reach back and catch the tops of the feet or the ankles with the hands. Push out with the shins and pull in with the arms keeping the elbows straight. Lift the chest and thighs off the ground. Head is up and back. Hold the position steady. Long Slow Deep Breathing. **1-3 minutes**.

continued on next page

Advanced Abdominal & Navel Strengthening

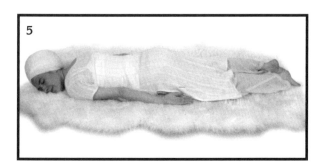

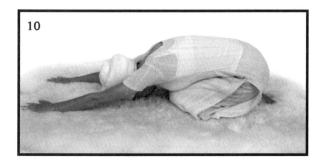

9. Rest on Stomach. Rest with normal breath on the stomach, arms by the sides with the head turned to the side. **1-3 minutes**.

10. Baby Pose Arms Extended. Push yourself up so that you are on the heels and place the forehead on the ground. Have the arms stretched out in front of the body on the ground with the hands shoulder width apart. Relax in this position with Normal Breath. **1-3 minutes**.

11. Camel Pose. Rise up out of the position and come up on to the knees. Reach back and place both hands on the heels. Arch the pelvis forward; keep the shoulders back and chest high. Either let the head fall all the way back or keep the chin on the chest. **1-3 minutes.**

12. Baby Pose. Release down onto the heels and place the forehead on the ground. Have the arms by the ankles with the palms up. Relax in this position with Normal Breath. **1-3 minutes**.

13. Deep Relaxation. Come out of position and rest on the back. Lie down flat, have the arms by the side palms up, with the eyes gently closed and the breath soft and normal. Have the knees up slightly for comfort, if needed.

COMMENTS
This kriya will center, strengthen, and balance the energy at the navel center. A strong navel center gives you boundless energy and the ability to transform yourself at will.

Firing Up the Metabolism

1. Lie down on the back. Raise the legs toward the ceiling and grasp the toes. Keep your legs up while you open and close them rapidly. Do Breath of Fire, timing the breath with the opening and closing of the legs. **5 1/2 minutes**.

2. Remain in the same position, holding onto your toes with the legs up. Pull the left foot toward the head. Let your left leg go back to the starting position as you pull your right foot toward your head. Continue alternately moving your legs up and down. Breath of Fire through the nose. **2 minutes**.

3. Continue the previous movement chanting *Har* with the tip of the tongue as each leg moves. Move quickly; chanting *Har* at a pace of two times per second. **12 minutes**.

4. Stay in the same position and combine the movements of exercises 1 and 2.

    Chant *Har* as your left leg moves up and down.
    Chant *Har* as your right leg moves up and down.
    Chant *Mukanday* as you open and close your legs.
One repetition of *Har Har Mukanday* takes 2 seconds.
Move quickly. **1 1/2 minutes**.

5. Sit up and relax for **1 minute**.

6. Sit in Easy Pose with the elbows bent and the palms facing forward at the level of the shoulders. The thumb and Sun Finger touch in Surya Mudra. Close your eyes and chant *Har Har Mukanday* rhythmically and musically for **11 minutes**. One repetition of the mantra takes **2 seconds**.

COMMENTS
The mantra *Har Har Mukanday* means Creative Infinity as Liberator.

VITALITY
Kriya to Become Super Human

1. This is a 4 part exercise. In a standing position, extend the left arm straight out in front, parallel to the ground. The left arm remains parallel to the ground for the entire sequence. Chant *Saa Taa Naa Maa* to the movements. **4 minutes**

    a) Bend forward at the waist on *Saa*

    b) Bend to the right on *Taa*

    c) Lean back on *Naa*

    d) Straighten back out on *Maa*

Saa   Taa   Naa   Maa

2. Remain standing and extend the right arm out straight in front of you, parallel to the ground.

Sequence is done to *Saa Taa Naa Maa* holding the extended arm still and maintaining balance. **2 minutes**

    a) Lift your left leg up to 90 degrees on *Saa*

    b) Still holding the leg up, turn your head to the right on *Taa*

    c) Still holding the leg up, turn your head to the left on *Naa*

    d) Bring your leg back down and your head to center on *Maa*

Saa   Taa   Naa   Maa

3. Same sequence as #2 only the left arm is extended out in front and it is the right leg that gets lifted straight out.
1 minute

Balance this brain, balance this cantaloupe. Below the Navel Point is independent of the sciatica. If that is so, old age will come, senility will come very early and creativity will be gone fast.

Kriya to Become Super Human

4. Still Standing in an upright position, lock the hands behind the neck and rapidly jump the knees up towards the chest. Legs come up together. Chant *Saa Taa Naa Maa* to the beat of the movement. This exercise must be done so that the knees touch the chest. **54-108 times**

You must develop your balance so that you land absolutely "cat footed." It is essential for a woman to have cat-footed balance, otherwise you can be inbalanced in the brain. 108 times will keep you intact.

5. Lie down flat on the back and elevate the legs 2 feet from the ground. Raise the head 2 feet from the ground. Clasp the hands in an arc over the navel point to balance the posture. Focus at the Third Eye Point. Inhale through the nose, exhale through the mouth like a hammer. **5 minutes**

You will be superhuman. 5 minutes of this breath is totally rejuvenating. No need for caffeine. If you can meditate like this for 5 minutes it equals meditating in a sitting position for 5 years. If you straighten out your back it will not hurt.

6. Sit in Virasan (on the left heel, right knee up to the chest). Arms extended straight out in front, parallel to the ground with palms facing down. Sing the *Chattr Chakkr Vartee* mantra powerfully for **22 minutes**:

> *Chattr chakkr vartee, chattr chakkr bhugtay*
> *Suyambhav subhang sarab daa sarab jugtay*
> *Dukaalang pranaasee dayaalang saroopay*
> *Sadaa ang sangay abhangang bibhootay*
>
> *You pervading and enjoying in all four directions,*
> *You are self-illumined and united with all.*
> *Destroyer of bad times, embodiment of mercy,*
> *You are ever within us, giver of undestroyable power.*
> —from Guru Gobind Singh's *Jaap Sahib*

Do this for 40 days and any positive wish will be fulfilled.

COMMENTS

This kriya can correct you and bring you to balance. Do it right and you will enjoy it. This is so powerful and effective; it self-maintains the body.

Inner Vitality & Stamina

1. Balance on the toes and fingertips with the knees straight but not locked. Rapidly move your hips from side to side like an animal swishing its tail.
3 minutes.

2. Sitting in Easy Pose, lean back to 60°. Fold the arms across the torso and lock the elbows with hands at diaphragm level. Keep your neck straight with your chin pulled in and roll your shoulders forward in a circle.
3 minutes.

3. Come into Baby Pose. Bring both hands to the small of the back and interlock the fingers. Raise your arms up into Yoga Mudra.
3 minutes.

Inner Vitality & Stamina

4. Cross the legs in Lotus Pose and lean back on the elbows. **3 minutes**.

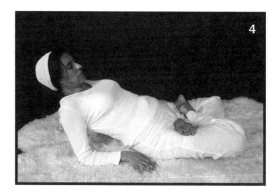

5. Stretch the legs out in front of you and grab your toes. Bring your head to your knees and come back up. Do this movement rapidly—**11 times only**. Breathe normally; do not do Breath of Fire.

6. Sit in Easy Pose, with your hands in Prayer Pose in the center of the chest. Focus the eyes at the tip of the nose. Keep your chin in, chest out and neck straight. Pump the Navel Point on the held breath, and imagine 30 trillion points of light in and around you.
3 minutes.

TO END: Inhale deeply, hold the breath and tighten every muscle of the body. Hold the breath for 10 seconds and then let it go out of the mouth explosively, like Cannon Fire. Repeat this 2 more times.

COMMENTS

The first exercise stimulates the endocrine system by stimulating the *tattvas* represented by each finger and the rush of blood to the higher glands at the Heart Center, head and neck. Exercises 3-5 test one's flexibility, a key indicator of vitality and youth. This kriya closes with the hands in Prayer Pose, aligning all the 10 Bodies at the Heart Center and visualizing your Self as 30 trillion points of light—every cell energized by the pump of the Navel Point.

VITALITY
Kriya to Take Away Stress

1. Sit on the heels, arms stretched out in front, right hand over left, thumbs locked. Lean the torso forward, arms straight and stretching from the shoulders. Put out your tongue and do Breath of Fire through the open mouth. **3 minutes**.
This breath adds strength to your nervous system.

2. Sit in Crow Pose and stretch your arms up and out at a 60 degree angle.
    a) Begin clapping your hands rapidly over your head as fast as you can, moving the entire arm from the shoulder. **30 seconds**.
    b) Then continue the motion, but instead of clapping, criss-cross the arms without touching. **2 1/2 minutes**.
This gives the mind basic strength and balances the nervous system.

3. Lie flat on your back, raise legs up to 90 degrees and begin criss-crossing the legs as fast as possible. **3 minutes**.
This exercise adjusts the Second Chakra and the sex organs.

Kriya to Take Away Stress

4. With hands under the hips, leaning on the elbows, raise legs up to 60 degrees. **3 minutes.**

This exercise can change the grey matter of the brain.

5. Sit in Baby Pose and with your hands pat your lower back rhythmically (the area of the 3rd, 4th, and 5th vertebrae and the kidney area). Pat with a slow relaxing rhythm. **2 1/2 minutes.**

6. Sit in Easy Pose with arms crossed in front of you at chin level, right arm over left. Straighten the spine, pull in the chin, close your eyes and chant the shabd *Rakhe Rakhanhar*, keeping the body absolutely still, no movement. **20 minutes.** Consciously use the tip of our tongue on the upper palate when chanting to stimulate the hypothalamus.

Rakhay rakhanhaar aap ubaarian
Gur kee pairee paa-eh kaaj savaarian
Hoaa aap dayaal manho na visaarian
Saadh janaa kai sang bhavjal taarian
Saakat nindak dusht khin maa-eh bidaarian
Tis saahib kee tayk naanak manai maa-eh
Jis simrat sukh ho-eh saglay dookh jaa-eh

God Himself is looking out for me,
Gives me the light, and takes care of my affairs.
God is merciful, and never forgets me.
God guides me, giving me good people to help me.
God does not allow any harm to come to me.
I take comfort in the thought of God.
When I remember God, I feel peaceful and happy and all my pain departs.

7. Lie down in Corpse Pose and relax. (If possible, listen to a gong meditation). **5 minutes.**

TO END: Briefly do cat stretch left and right, raise and lower shoulders, roll neck loosely, stretch rib cage, roll digestive area, stretch hands, wiggle toes, blink, move lips and roll tongue around the front of the teeth.

COMMENTS

Yoga is a science through which a person can use his mental, physical, and spiritual being to tap into the Infinity of God. This set is designed to take away stress so that we can totally enjoy what we are living for.

Meditation for Mental Energy & Glandular Balance

1. Sit in Easy Pose. The left hand holds the right elbow. The right hand is in front of the right shoulder. The arms make an L. Make a fist of the right hand with the thumb at the base of the Mercury finger and the fingers curled around the thumb. The fist faces the midline of the body and should be so tight that it hurts to release it. Eyes at the tip of the nose. Whistle with *Ardas Bhaee*, instrumental version. **11 minutes**.

2. Interlace the hands behind the base of the spine straightening the arms so the chest is pushed forward. Sway the upper body and head as one, left and right with the music. Sway 18 inches from the base of the spine—9 inches to each side while mentally following the sound. Music: *Sat Nam Wahe Guru* by Lata Mangeskar. **2 1/2 minutes**.

3. Extend the arms in front of you in Prayer Pose with the thumbs locked. Begin a chopping motion with the arms—like an axe—bring the arms all the way up and lower them all the way down. Music: Tantric Har. Chant along with the motion of the arms. **1 1/2 minutes**.

TO END: Inhale and stretch up. Suspend the breath for 10 seconds. Cannon Fire exhale. Repeat. Once again inhale and stretch up maximum. Suspend the breath for 5 seconds. Exhale and relax.

Note: Yogi Bhajan does not indicate an eye position for parts two and three of this meditation.

Kriya for Energy & Rejuvenation

1. Grab the edge of a sink, stable chair, or your partner, and walk the feet back until you are holding your body at a 45 degree slope from heels to head. You will feel a stretch in your hamstrings. Begin raising and lowering alternate heels, walking in place without lifting the toes off the ground. Arms and legs are fully extended and the body bends slightly in the middle. As you walk, you may lower your head, it does not have to be held up. Walk vigorously and work up a sweat. **11 minutes**.

2. Stand with the feet shoulder width apart and extend the arms above your head with the palms facing forward, the elbows slightly bent, and the fingers spread wide apart. Swing your arms from side to side, keeping the hands above shoulder level. The momentum of the arm swing will cause the hips to swing if you are doing the movement with enough force. Continue **11 minutes**.

3. Once again grab the edge of the sink, stable chair, or a partner. Bend at the waist with your head down between your arms. You will feel a stretch in your lower back and in the backs of your legs. Relax and stretch for **11 minutes**.

COMMENTS
This set is to be done at the bathroom sink or someplace where you have a partner, a bar or a support to hold on to.

VITALITY
Sanmukh Kriya

PART ONE

Sit in Easy Pose. Chin slightly into the chest. Raise the chest slightly. Pull the lower spine forward slightly.

EYES: Focused on the tip of the nose.

MUDRA: Palms face forward at the level of the face, to the sides of each shoulder, about 12 inches away from each ear and just slightly forward of vertical. All fingers point straight up. Bend the sun fingers and place the pads of this finger on top of the sun mount, the fleshy part of the palm directly at the base of the sun finger. Hold it down with the thumb pressing on the nail of the ring finger. Lock yourself in this position.

MANTRA: Meditate silently while listening to the mantra

Sat Siree, Siree Akaal
Siree Akaal, Maaha Akaal
Maaha Akaal, Sat Naam
Akaal Moorat, Wah-hay Guroo
Great Truth, Great beyond Death
Great beyond Death, the Great Undying
Truth is His Name, Deathless Image of God
Great Beyond Words is this Wisdom.

TIME: **11 minutes**. Do not exceed this time limit.

COMMENTS
"You and God shall sit face to face when you will perfect this kriya. I am giving it to you because you are my future. This will give you strength and wings. It will take you away from weaknesses. It will give you vitality. Sometimes you may want to overdose on this meditation. But do not extend this for more than 11 minutes at one time. Why? If you become a perfect practitioner of it, you'll reach a state of non-existence, and then there'll be trouble. You'll start moving the whole world, and you will not like to move yourself. You are young people and it'll ruin your life. Then you can sit and say, "Okay, somebody should go to my office and do the work." And somebody will get up from the house and represent you and do your work. There's no human who can refuse you, there's no power which shall not bow to you. There's no situation which shall not obey you."

—YOGI BHAJAN (speaking to a group of teenagers.)

Sanmukh Kriya

PART TWO

MUDRA: Maintain the same posture as in Part One.

EYES: Focused on the tip of nose.

MANTRA: Chant the mantra *Wahe Guru*, in a very particular fashion, pulling three locks as you chant. Break it into three parts:

Whaa - hay Guroo

Whaa and **Hay** are run together in one continuous sound with no break, but there is a slight emphasis on the **Whaa**.

On **Whaa**, pull the Root Lock (anus, sex organs, and navel) in very sharply. There will be a brief pause at the end of **Whaa**. **Whaa** is chanted short and fast.

On **hay** you pull the Navel Point powerfully, even further in and up, pulling in the Diaphragm Lock, also.

On **Guroo** you apply the Neck Lock—then release and begin again.

If done properly, you will feel an upward circular movement of the energy, "like a roller." The belly must come in, come up toward the diaphragm, and then release.

TIME: **11 minutes**

COMMENTS

"This meditation will give you a powerful projection of a thought. It invokes the pure energy of the navel.

Wahe Guru is a trikutee mantra, the mantra of the Ajna Chakra or Third Eye. If not chanted properly, it does nothing. When the Root Lock, Diaphragm Lock and the Neck Lock are applied all together, it is called Great Lock or mahabandh. And when a person perfects maha bandh, he controls the universe just with his thought. Whaa is a water sound. If you pour a bottle of water, it'll sound like whaa, whaa, whaa. There is 60 percent water in you. You will have control of water. If you say hay properly by turning the middle of the tongue, hay will sound very effective. If your sound hay becomes perfect, send a mental message, job is done. Once in a while when I'm tired, I don't want to make a phone call because I don't remember the number, so I just send the mental message, and then ring, and I say, "Hi, I was going to call you." I should not use it, but sometimes I am tired. Too much work. If the word guroo becomes perfect with you, you can stop a moving truck. You can stop the movements of the entire universe into shuniya—stillness. There is no power which is not with you. If you harness it, it is yours. If you waste it, you've lost it."

—YOGI BHAJAN

continued on next page

VITALITY
Sanmukh Kriya

PART THREE

Sit in Easy Pose. Chin in. Chest out. Spine straight. Interlace the fingers, and place the hands, palms flat, against the back of the head. Elbows are bent and extended straight out to the sides. (Don't let them droop—no angles.)

EYES: Closed.

MANTRA: Chant the following mantra out loud:

Sat Naam, Sat Naam, Sat Naam Jee
Whaa-hay Guroo Whaa-hay Guroo Whaa-hay Guroo Jee
Truth is my identiy, or dear soul
Great is the ecstasy of knowing that identity.

Use a recording of the same name.

TIME: **11 minutes**

Boundless Strength

Lie on the back.

MUDRA: Bring the arms and legs up to 90°. Arms and legs are shoulder-width apart and the palms of the hands are open and facing each other.

MUSIC: Nirinjan Kaur's recording of *Say Saraswati* was played. You may chant along with the music.

TIME: **31 minutes**.

COMMENTS
This exercise renews the spine.

Throw Off Stress & Uncover Your Strength

Sit in Easy Pose with a straight spine.

1. Bring the hands up by the shoulders with the palms forward and the fingers pointing upward. Touch the thumb and the Jupiter finger and then touch the thumb and the Sun finger. Continue rapidly touching the thumb alternately with each of the two fingers. Concentrate on the tip of your nose. Keep the eyes open. The ideal speed for this action is 9 touches per second, but 3 touches per second is acceptable.

    After **5 1/2 minutes**, begin inhaling and exhaling powerfully through the mouth. Breathe through the mouth for **2 minutes** and then begin Breath of Fire through the nose for another **30 seconds**. Inhale deeply and relax.
This exercise adjusts the ovaries, stimulates the life force energy, and releases stress.

2. Cross the hands over the Heart Center, left hand on top of right. Close the eyes and breathe extremely deeply and slowly as you feel the healing strength of your own hands on your heart. **4 minutes**.

3. Put both hands on the forehead, feeling the healing effect of your hands. Concentrate on "I am, I am" as you listen to Nirinjan Kaur's recording of *Bountiful, Beautiful, and Blissful.* **7 minutes**.

4. Put both hands on the Navel Point and press with all your force. Breathe slowly and meditate deeply on Nirinjan Kaur's recording of *Ong Namo Guru Dev Namo.* **8 minutes**.
TO END: Inhale deeply, open your eyes and shake your hands.

Throw Off Stress & Uncover Your Strength

5. Twist your wrists back and forth, keeping the five fingers spread open. **2 minutes**.

This is to change the neurons of the brain.

6. Put the hands on the shoulders and sing along with Guru Shabad Singh's recording of *Pavan Pavan*, while you make your shoulders dance to the music. **5 minutes**.

Dance to free your rib cage. Your total health will benefit by opening up your rib cage in this movement. It's a partnerships between you and your shoulders, not just an up and down movement. Do it with style.

7. Use your open palms to beat your inner thighs. Use the rhythm of the recording *Punjabi Drums* to pace your movement. **3 1/2 minutes**.

This self-massage will balance the calcium and magnesium in your body and reduce the effects of old age.

COMMENTS

Though this kriya can be done by both men and women, when he taught it, Yogi Bhajan was teaching to a class of women. This is what he said about this kriya:

"To be a woman requires a lot of strength. Your glandular system, your intelligence and your consciousness have to be extraordinarily strong so you can be on the winning side. All the strength of the Universe is within you. It cannot be found outside. Those who do not develop strength from inside cannot get it from outside either."

Invincible Man Exercises

1. Find a partner. Sit in Easy Sitting Pose opposite each other and touch hands—palm to palm. Look at one another straight in the eyes and repeat this mantra, *"I love myself. I forgive you."*

   a) As you say, *"I love myself,"* bring your hands to Prayer Pose at the heart.

   b) As you say, *"I forgive you,"* bring your hands palm-to-palm with your partner. Continue the movement with each repetition of the mantra. Experience what it does. Look like a man. **4 minutes**

2. Still seated, looking into your partner's eyes, continue the movement with the mantra, *"Peace"*. With each repetition of *"Peace,"* move from Prayer Pose to palm-to-palm. **2 1/2 minutes**

3. Come standing on your knees facing your partner.

   a) Bring your hands together in Prayer Pose and say, *"Love."*

   b) Come palm-to-palm with your partner and say, *"Peace."* This exercise is very important because you are relating to your sciatica. **2 1/2 minutes**

4. Continue standing on you knees facing your partner, looking eye-to-eye. Stretch your arms out to each side, palms down.

   a) Move the arms up and down (about 12 inches) to a count of four.

   b) On five, clap hands with your partner and alternately chant *Peace!* or *Love!* Move the arms 1-2-3-4-Peace! (clap); 1-2-3-4-Love! (clap). Continue for **9 1/2 minutes**

Invincible Man Exercises

5. Camel Pose. Standing on the knees, press the pelvis forward and lift the heart as your reach back for your heels. Allow the head to drop back. Chant *"I will never bite the bait."* This is the only way you will remember it. There is no other way. **3 minutes**

6. Come standing up and take your partner's hands.
   a) Slowly sit down and repeat, *"Let us sit in peace."*
   b) Slowly rise and say, *"Let us rise in consciousness."*
4 minutes

7. Sit on the heels and bend back, putting your weight on your elbows. Bring the hands into fists near the shoulders. Your head will automatically fall back. Keep this posture as you sing the entire *Ardas Bhaee* mantra. The energy will adjust itself. You will see how this burnout is going to work out. Sing with it.
5 minutes

> **Ardaas bhayee, Amar daas guroo**
> **Amar daas guroo, Ardaas bhayee**
> **Raam daas guroo, Raam daas guroo,**
> **Raam daas guroo, Sachee sahee**
>
> *The prayer is offered, oh Guru Amar Das!*
> *Guru Ram Das, Guru Ram Das,*
> *Guru Ram Das, truly seals it*

Hold the posture and keep the pressure. It will make changes in you. It may feel a little painful now, but it will bring fantastic strength. It is very healing, very good. Make a fist of your hands. This will break the crystallization in the muscle and the nerves. It will break obstacles in the energy flow.

continued on next page

Invincible Man Exercises

8a, 8c

8b

8d

9

8. Sit in Easy Sitting Pose. Make fists with your hands and bring them in front of the shoulders. Repeat *"I am, I am."* Chant loudly and powerfully. Let the God hear you! **8 minutes**

    a) *"I"* the hands are at the shoulders
    b) *"Am"* the arms extend out to the sides—straight.
    c) *"I"* the hands are at the shoulders
    d) *"Am"* the arms extend straight up

9. Sit facing your partner, eye-to-eye. Bring your hands into fists in front of your face—about eye level. Repeat *"I am, I am."* Communicate your pure *"I am"* to each other. As you talk, so your hands should move to explain your expression. Fists tight. Talk with lips and fists. Talk and fists should indicate the language. **9 minutes**

10. Sit facing your partner, eye-to-eye. Bring your hands up. Spread your fingers open and move the arms stiffly. Try to part the wind. Do it fast, powerfully, and strongly. The hands must move the heavens, the earth and the stars. No bend. Powerfully and steadily. The whole body will move if you do it right. Make the whole body a unit. You must move the whole body, not just the hands.

10 minutes

TO END: Inhale and hold the breath for 30 seconds. Mentally vibrate the mantra God and me, me and God are one. Repeat. Relax.

10

CHAPTER NINE

RESILIENCE

MASTERING THE SELF

"Keep Up!"

"That's all you need, this one, simple psychological, transformation, this one word, "Keep up"—cherdi kala. Keep up means cherdi kala. Against all odds, keep going; that's what Guru said, and that's what we have to learn."

–Yogi Bhajan

Strong as steel, steady as stone, is a phrase that embodies the idea of resilience. In the face of anything and everything, to be steady, unflinching, calm—that is the consciousness of a yogi. And that is the consciousness required to serve throughout this change of the Age. This world of maya is a pressure cooker. Our nervous and glandular systems must be up for the task of balancing our emotional, commotional reactions and emerging neutral, aware and conscious. We must be able to command ourselves, our minds, and our bodies, under any circumstances. If not, we will continue to be slaves to the ego instead of servants of Infinity.

We must not only be able to command, but also co-ordinate our psyche so that our reflexes serve our mission rather than undermine our goals. The tools and technologies in this chapter deliver you beyond fatigue, exhaustion and emotional compensation and develop your capacity to command your reflexes, cultivate positivity in your projection and balance your polarity in order to build and sustain longevity throughout the life course.

We must be able to withstand the pressure of the times so that we can serve the times—and heal them! For if not us, who? And if not now, when? This is our task.

"It is the responsibility of all of us to grow. We must start healing the world, which is going to come at us, so this is the time to grow. Grow and glow, hail and heal, and keep going. Stop this, 'I have a cough, I have a cold, I'm this, I'm that.' Whatever is wrong is wrong.

Sing a song, 'I'm wrong, wrong is wrong, there's nothing wrong, get going, keep going,' something like that. The word, 'Keep up!' is the most, well-coined phrase. Count all your curses and say, 'Curses you are dead! I'm keeping up!' That's all you need, this one, simple psychological, transformation, this one word, "Keep up"—cherdi kala. Keep up means cherdi kala. Against all odds, keep going; that's what Guru said, and that's what we have to learn."

–Yogi Bhajan, December 31, 1995

Ever uplifting spirit—*cherdi kala*—is the movement of the kundalini and the consciousness of the spiritual warrior, the one who has come to serve the Aquarian Age. All of us are here at this unique space and time to manifest our collective destiny. But to get there, and to get there together, we need a tremendous amount of tolerance, grace and resilience.

The question is not whether we will be tested—the question is whether or not we will pass the test. Build your Self to act, not react. Be positive, even in the face of a seemingly insurmountable negativity. Be neutral, in the presence of increasing polarity. For when all seems lost, we must be ready to lead. And who could be better to guide the way out than we who have passed through the fire, together?

Be your own flame, purify your Self, define and refine your identity in Infinity so that your resilience is known to you and to others. Become the diamond in the crown of the one who holds the throne of Raj Yog and heal yourself that you may heal the world.

RESILIENCE
Withstand the Pressure of Time

1. Sit in Easy Pose, raise the arms up with bent elbows and begin shaking the whole body. It should be an inward body massage. Every muscle and fiber must shake. Arms, body and head must move. Create your own rhythm and style. Generate some heat. **15 minutes**.
This will release toxins from your muscles. Get wild. Shake like an earthquake. It would take hours of massage to get to this point. Cheeks should get red. You must come to the dead end of tiredness.

2. Come standing up straight. Shake the hips from side to side by bending the knees alternately. Feet can either stay on the ground and hands can dangle loosely, or vigorously twist the hips and jump in the air while pumping your arms. **8 minutes**.
Make this an energetic dance. Your thigh muscles should sweat. This will get rid of toxins and the tissue deposits. This will get out the old anger in your body.

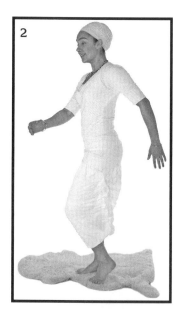

3. In Easy Pose, extend the arms straight over the head with palms together, arms against the ears. Twist the body left and right. **4 minutes**.
It is a triangular move. If done powerfully, it will release your shoulders.

4. On the hands and knees, lift the left leg straight out behind you. Touch the forehead to the ground and come back up, like push-ups. **52 times**. Repeat with right leg. **52 times**.

Withstand the Pressure of Time

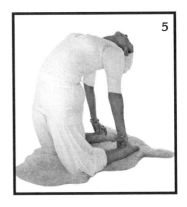

5. Come standing on your knees and bend back into Camel Pose, resting the hands on the heels. Straighten back up onto the knees. Alternate between Camel Pose and standing on the knees. **55 times**.

6. Lie down flat on the back.

a) Lift the knees up to the chest and place the hands under the hips. You may elevate the hips with the hands slightly, in order to get the knees to the chest.

b) Extend the legs straight out.

c) Raise the legs up to 90 degrees.

Then bring the knees back to the chest. **108 times**.

This movement gives power for your prana to be controlled by will. It is the movement of the Pavanmuktasana, where the prana is controlled by will.

7. Lie down flat and put both hands over the Heart Center and relax. Sit up and bring the forehead to the knees and relax back down on the back. **26 times**.

8. Corpse Pose. Lie down flat on the back for a deep relaxation. If a gong is available, make this a gong meditation.
8 minutes.

You will become weightless and enjoy it. Relax.

COMMENTS

This is a powerful and energetic kriya for a full tune-up of the nervous system. If the nerves are not tuned-up you will not be able to withstand the pressure of the time. This also works on two problems common to a woman—locked up pelvis and locked shoulders.

Beyond Fatigue

1. Come into Camel Pose. Breathe powerfully through the nose with one complete breath every 2 to 3 seconds. Inhale deeply to fill the lungs, and as you exhale press the navel forcefully toward the spine. Continue for **4 minutes**.

This exercise is effective in the treatment of water and food diseases. It helps reduce obesity and, with regular practice, "gives one the power to live forty days without food."

Variation: You can also do this to music, using *Jaap Sahib* recording by Ragi Sat Nam Singh. Chant with the music and breathe powerfully and rhythmically. Press the navel in on the accented syllables of *Namastang* and *Namo*. Continue through Verse 28. (The next verse begins with Chaachree Chand Tav Prasad.)

2. Come into Crow Pose. Keep the spine straight and the feet flat on the ground. Extend the arms straight out in front, parallel to the ground with the hands in fists. Maintaining a tension in the arms, move the arms alternately 30 degrees above and 30 degrees below parallel, with one arm rising as the other descends. Continue for **2 minutes**.
(Musical variation: Chant along with Jaap Sahib.)

3. Lie on the back and interlock the hands behind the neck at the hairline. Raise the legs, hips, buttocks and torso off the floor in an arching, jumping motion. Let the body drop down and hit hard on the floor. Continue for **4 minutes**.
This is a good exercise for the lower back and is "the best thing a woman can do for herself."

4. Sit in Easy Pose. Extend the arms out to the sides, palms facing down. The right arm is 30 degrees above parallel, left arm 30 degrees below parallel. Keep the arms straight, moving them together in one line. The right arm lowers to the floor, slapping the ground 4 times as the left arm rises and make the same slapping motion in the air. Move to the rhythm of the mantra *Har Har Har Haree*. **3 minutes**. Chant this mantra powerfully in a monotone from the Navel Center behind the belly button.

5. Remain in Easy Pose and move the arms as in Exercise 4 with the mantra *Har Har Whaa-hay Guroo.* On the fifth beat, *Guroo*, do a quick double-strike with the hands. Continue for **3 minutes**.

6. Repeat Exercise 5 chanting the mantra twice per side for **3 minutes**.

Beyond Fatigue

7. Continue chanting **Har Har Whaa-hay Guroo.** as you proceed through the following postures. Each is done for 30 seconds.
   a) Place the right hand on the heart and tap the ground with the left hand.
   b) Continue with both arms as in Exercise 4.
   b) Repeat 7a.
   c) Repeat 7b.
   d) Repeat 7a.

This is a brain exercise which strengthens the electromagnetic field. The upper arm motion is said to bring youthfulness and the motion of the lower arm, or striking arm, brings you energy.

8. Sit in Easy Pose. Extend the arms straight in front parallel to the ground, hands in fists. Powerfully move both arms alternately 30 degrees above and 30 degrees below parallel. Move like a fast and powerful machine. Begin with Breath of Fire, then substitute the mantra **Saa Taa Naa Maa** in rhythm with the arm movement. Continue for **2 minutes.**

9. Sit in Easy Pose with the hands in Gyan Mudra resting on the knees. Breathe through the nose long and gently, experiencing peace and compassion. Meditate and feel healed throughout. Continue this healing meditation for **5 to 10 minutes.**
Musical Variation: using a version of *Dhan Dhan Ram Das Gur.* Sing openly from the heart.

10. Lie on your back with the arms by the sides, palms facing up. Deeply relax for **10 minutes.**

COMMENTS
Stress is endemic in our society. It can never be completely avoided so its negative effects must be counteracted in the body. One of the victims of chronic stress is the endocrine system. These glands are charged with adjusting the chemical balance in the blood and, in turn, the experience of well being. Chronic fatigue and attempts to self-medicate using caffeine are often signs that stress has led to poor adrenal function.

This kriya is beneficial in strengthening the adrenal glands and relieving the long-term effects of stress. The adrenal glands play a very important role in the overall health of the body, mind and spirit. They produce hormones which control the body's automatic functions of breath rate, heartbeat and digestion and determine whether the body is relaxed or alert.

This set of exercises strengthens the adrenal glands, improves digestion, balances the nervous system and the brain's hemispheres, helps alleviate fear and invigorates the body.

RESILIENCE
Coordinating Body, Mind & Soul

1. Sit in Easy Pose. With the fingers relaxed and open, use your thumbs to massage the ear mound, the flap that attaches to the cheek. **1 minute.**

2. Reach the hands up over your head and interlock the fingers. Stretch up as you move your body in an upward spiral from the base of the spine. Feel like you are going upward, keeping your elbows and spine straight. This spiral must stretch your spine up half an inch, minimum. **4 1/2 minutes.**

3. Stay in the same position and make three spirals upward and then bend forward, stretching the arms along the ground, touching the forehead to the floor. Keep your elbows straight. Rise up and repeat the entire motion, continuing for **3 1/2 minutes.**

4. Victory Pose. Lie down on the back with the hands by your sides. Raise the arms and legs up so that you are balanced on your pelvic bone. Focus the eyes on the tips of the toes. Pump your navel without breath of fire. **5 minutes.**

5. Repeat exercise two, making **52 spirals.**

6. Stretch the arms overhead, open the fingers wide, and shake your hands vigorously. Shake so that your whole body shakes. This will break up the toxin patterns in the body. **1 1/2 minutes.**

Coordinating Body, Mind & Soul

7. Squat down in Frog Pose so the buttocks are on the heels. The heels are touching, and off the ground. Put the fingertips on the ground between the knees. Keep the head up. Inhale, straighten legs up, keeping the fingers on the ground and relax the head. Exhale and come back squatting down, face forward. The inhale and exhale should be strong. Continue this cycle **52 times**.

8. Bowing *Jaap Sahib*. Sit on the heels with the arms stretched overhead and the fingers interlocked. Bow your forehead to the ground and rise back up. Move to the rhythm of Ragi Sat Nam Singh's recording of *Jaap Sahib*. **108 times**.

9. Sit up straight, cross the hands over the heart. Listen to Ragi Sat Nam Singh's recording of *Jaap Sahib*. **13 minutes**.

10. Sing along with the recording of *Chattr Chakkr Vartee* by Pritpal Singh. Sing from your heart. This mantra takes fear out of your life. **6 minutes**.

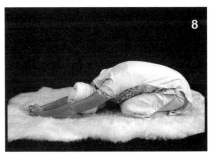

Chattr chakkr vartee, chattr chakkr bhugtay
Suyambhav subhang sarab daa sarab jugtay
Dukaalang pranaasee dayaalang saroopay
Sadaa ang sangay abhangang bibhootay

You pervading and enjoying in all four directions,
You are self-illumined and united with all.
Destroyer of bad times, embodiment of mercy,
You are ever within us, giver of undestroyable power.
      —from Guru Gobind Singh's *Jaap Sahib*

Build Yourself to Act, Not React

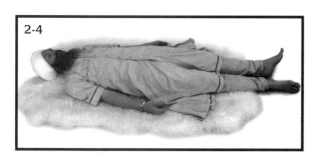

1. Stretch the legs straight out in front. Grab the toes and stretch the spine forward. Inhale and tilt the head up, stretching the back of your neck. Exhale and bring your chin to your chest. Maintain the stretch in the spine. Continue to move your head with the breath, being careful not to compress the vertebrae of the neck. Breathe in and out fast and powerfully. **1 1/2 minutes**.

2. Lie down on the back, begin Breath of Fire, and dance your body. Move any way you wish, but don't raise any part of your body off the floor. No part should be stable, all parts should move. It's a physically violent reaction to get rid of internal violence in a controlled fashion. It's "you against you." Take all the pain out, don't hold anything in. **3 1/2 minutes**.

3. Relax on your back. Go to sleep. Listen to the tape of the gong meditation played by Yogi Bhajan. Bring your strength to your toes and go with the gong. The three rhythms of the gong will work on the glandular system. If you give yourself a good chance, it will work on the pineal gland. **11 minutes**.
(Note: In order to receive the benefits of this set, it is required that you meditate to the gong meditation played by Yogi Bhajan.)

4. Move feet and hands, wake yourself up.

5. Sit in Easy Pose. Chant: *God and Me, Me and God, Are One* meditatively going from chakra to chakra. **15 minutes**.

God & me   me & God are   one

TO END: Inhale and hold your breath **20-30 seconds** and stretch your body. Exhale. Inhale and move your body all around, stimulating your energy. **30 seconds**. Exhale and relax.

Emotional Fatigue Buster

Sit in a meditative posture with the spine straight. Chin in and chest out.

1. The right hand is up with the elbow relaxed down and the palm facing out. The Saturn and Sun fingers are split—the "Vulcan" greeting—locking the Jupiter and Saturn fingers together and the Sun and Mercury fingers together. The left hand is palm down, fingers spread wide, with the elbow relaxed by the side. Move the left hand back and forth. The hand moves like a pendulum, one complete stroke—left and right—per second. Breathe through a firm **O-shaped mouth**, keeping pace with the movement of the left hand. **11 minutes**.

TO END: Inhale deeply and interlace the fingers and stretch them above the head. Stretch. Exhale. Repeat twice more and relax.
Note: Do not practice longer than **11 minutes**.

It will take away your internal fatigue forever. The fatigue, which your body cannot remove, which makes you old, which makes you weak, will disappear in the first 7 minutes. Yawning is natural, normal. Let it come.

2. Move the arms vigorously—your entire torso moves—go wild!
3 minutes.

No music is played so that you don't become systematic, rhythmic. Go wild!

3. Bring the tips of the thumb, Jupiter, and Saturn fingers of each hand together, then lift and swing the arms alternately back over the head in a bicycle-like motion. Move quickly. **1 minute**.

4. Release the mudra and sit straight. Whistle loudly with the instrumental version of *Ardas Bhaee*. **4 minutes**.

    Begin singing if you know the words. **1 1/2 minutes**.
    Whisper the mantra. **1 minute**.
    Whistle. **30 seconds**.

TO END: Inhale deeply. Concentrate at the Navel Point. Hold the breath. Pull the navel in toward the spine. Exhale. Repeat twice more.

Developing the Command Reflexes & Alertness

1a, 2d

This entire set repeats for a total of two times in one sitting.

1. This is a 4-part exercise done in Easy Pose, to the beat and sound of
   SAA TAA NAA MAA
   a) **SAA**: arms extend straight out, level with the heart. Hands clap in front.
   b) **TAA**: arms open straight out to the side with palms facing up.
   c) **NAA**: arms are still out to the side buy palms turn over, facing down.
   d) **MAA**, hands will clap straight over the head.
   1 minute.

1b, 2c

2. Reverse the sequence of exercise #1, still chanting:
   SAA TAA NAA MAA
   a) **SAA**: Clap the hands over the head.
   b) **TAA**: Extend arms straight out to the sides with palms facing down.
   c) **NAA**: Arms still out to the sides, flip the palms facing up.
   d) **MAA**: Clap hands straight out in front of you.
   2 minutes.

1c, 2b

3. This is a 4-beat exercise done with the mantra **SAA TAA NAA MAA**. Sit on the heels, and clasp the hands behind the back in Yoga Mudra (interlacing fingers behind the back, palms facing up.)
a) **SAA**: Stand up on your knees.
b) **TAA**: Bend over and put the forehead on the ground and raise the arms in Yoga Mudra up behind your back as far as they will go. Buttocks are not resting on the heels.

1d, 2a

c) **NAA**: Rise back up, still standing on your knees, arms will rest back down on your back in Yoga Mudra.
d) **MAA**: Sit back down on the heels, arms still positioned in relaxed Yoga Mudra. **2 minutes.**   *This is a great waist reduction exersise.*

3a, 3c

3b

3d

Developing the Command Reflexes & Alertness

4. Another 4-part exercise done to the mantra *SAA TAA NAA MAA*. In a standing position clasp your hands in Yoga Mudra behind your back.

a) *SAA:* Bend forward at the waist bringing your forehead as close to your legs as you can, with hands interlocked in Yoga Mudra. Raise your arms as high above the back as they can go.

b) *TAA:* Straighten back up with arms relaxed down, still in Yoga Mudra behind the back.

4b, 4d

4a

4c

c) *NAA:* Arch backwards as far as you can, leading with your head. Arms are in relaxed Yoga Mudra behind you.

d) *MAA:* Stand back up straight with your arms relaxed in Yoga Mudra behind you. **2 minutes**.

5. This is another 4-part rhythmic exercise in a standing position.

1) Start in a standing position, hands in Yoga Mudra clasped behind the back. Raise left knee up as high as you can, and raise the arms up behind you simultaneously as high as you can. Keep the body fairly straight.

2) The same action, only raising your right knee up.

3) Repeat a.

4) Repeat b.

This is a command, obedience exercise. The teacher counts out "1,2,3,4" at a fast pace, occasionally mixing up order. Listen and follow as exactly called.

4 minutes.

1 & 3

2 & 4

Reflexes for the Vital Core

Sit in Easy Pose.

1.Cover the ears with the hands. The Venus Mound at the base of the thumb is just behind the cheekbone. The palms cover the ears with the fingers pointing up and aiming slightly behind the head. Press and release both hands. Apply 25 pounds of pressure to the head and then release the hands away from the head about 3-6 inches. *(Nirinjan Kaur's Humee Hum Brahm Hum was played in class.)* **22 minutes**.

Note: For the final 3 minutes, increase the pace of the press/release; move quickly.

TO END: Press the skull with the hands and inhale and hold for **15-20 seconds**. Cannon Fire exhale keeping the pressure constant. Repeat twice more.

2. Break for **10 minutes**. Relax, talk, enjoy.

3. Place the hands on the seventh rib, just beneath the line of the breasts. The thumbs point up toward the shoulder and the fingers point toward each other. Move the hands upward and inward—very fast! The breasts will move. Don't be shy. Look at the tip of the nose. Meditate and massage your seventh rib. *(Punjabi Drums was played in class.)* **11 minutes.**

TO END: Inhale deep and hold tight for 10–25 seconds. Press the ribs. Cannon Fire exhale. Repeat twice more.

Reflexes for the Vital Core

4. Break for **6 minutes**. Shake out your hands and shoulders for a few seconds and then relax.

5. Put the base of your palm on the cheekbones; the fingers point up and rest at the top of the forehead. Squeeze the hands up and in toward the nose, pressing on the cheekbone. The hands will cover the eyes. Move in a steady, rhythmic pattern. *(Punjabi Drums was played in class.)*   **11 minutes**.

6. Stand up and dance with a partner. After **6 minutes**, keep dancing and move your hands up and down above your head and continue to move your feet. Continue for **3 minutes**.

7. Sit down.
   a) Rest the hands on the heart; right hand over left. Breathe long, slow and deep, consciously. Try to breathe four breaths per minute. *(Nirinjan Kaur's recording of Say Saraswati was played throughout the rest of the class.)*
   Close the eyes and go deeply within. **6 minutes**.
   Gong meditation for **6 minutes**.
   Continue meditating, breathing slowly, consciously. **2 minutes**.

   b) Now begin clapping with the breath. Clap once on the inhale; clap once on the exhale. Find your rhythm. **3 1/2 minutes**.

   c) Bring the hands together in Prayer Pose at the Heart Center and put maximum pressure on the hands. Breathe slowly and deeply. **3 1/2 minutes**. Inhale deep and hold for **20 seconds**. Relax.

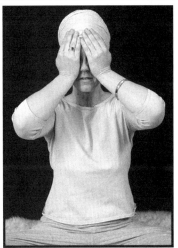

Emotional Resilience: Cutting Negative Thoughts

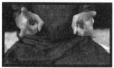

1. Press the Sun and Mercury finger down tightly with the thumb. Spread the Jupiter and Saturn into a V. Place them in front of the chest facing each other with the fingers pointing straight ahead. Press the elbows into the ribs. Fully open and close them, quickly, like scissors. After **3 minutes** begin continuously pulling only your most negative thoughts from your subconscious. Pull them out. Keep scissoring your hands and cutting the thoughts. **11 minutes**.

You are cutting your your bad thoughts, your misfortune, your everything. Even in spite of that, you will feel miserable in another half minute.

If I tell you that after you do this for half an hour you will be a king, you will be, but you will be a miserable king, because this exercise does it. It's automatic. It is just the Jupiter and Saturn finger and your Sun and Mercury is tied down by your ego. So minus your ego, you are doing something. God, it will put you inside out. But keep on doing it fast enough. The faster and fuller you do it, the better the result will be. And it will be proportionately less, if you cheat. Qualify, qualify, qualify, it's worthwhile.

a) Keep moving the fingers and begin Cannon Breath without rounding the lips. **90 seconds.**

b) Keep moving the fingers and begin to create a 'pa pa' sound, the basic bij sound, from the natural movement of the lips. Don't speak the sound. Continue to bring up negative thoughts and cut them. **90 seconds.**

c) Keep moving the fingers and continuing the 'pa pa' sound. Now imagine that you're abusing someone with your mouth and lips. First become obnoxious and then abusive in your thought. Pull the negative, obnoxious and abusive thoughts up to the surface and release them. **90 seconds.**
Inhale deeply and relax

2. Clasp the hands behind the neck. Move the elbows in and out as you dance from the Navel Point upward. Be forceful, angry, wild while your lower body remains a solid base. Music: *Punjabi Drums.* **6 minutes.**

3. Inhale and immediately bring your arms up straight overhead. Spread the fingers wide, not letting them touch.
Cannon Breath. **60 to 90 seconds**. Inhale deeply and stretch up. Exhale.
Inhale, stretch up and hold for **20 seconds.**
Inhale, stretch and do cannon breath quickly for **15 seconds**. Exhale.
Inhale, hold for **20 seconds**. Stretch and pull up every bit of you.
Exhale and relax.

Longevity Kriya

Sit in Easy Pose.

1. Raise the right arm up to sixty degrees in front of you. Bring the left arm in a sixty degree angle pointing downward behind you. The two arms should form a straight 60-degree line. Keep the elbows stretched. The palm of the right hand mudra is downward and the palm of the left hand mudra is upward. The closed eyes are focused at the center of the chin, the Moon Center. Breathe slowly and deeply. Sit with a straight spine and let your body go through its changes, through each of the following parts:

a) Jupiter finger of each hand is extended with the thumb locking down the other fingers. **3 minutes**.

b) In the same position, extend the Mercury finger with the Jupiter finger. Lock the other fingers down with the thumb. **3 minutes**.

c) Still maintaining the arm position, extend all the fingers. Tighten all the muscles of the body and stretch the arms. Eyes remain focused at the center of the chin. Continue to breathe slowly and deeply. **3 minutes**.
This will kill any disease in the body.

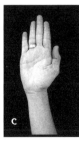

TO END: Inhale, hold the breath for **10 seconds**, stretch and tighten all the muscles of the body. Exhale and repeat this sequence two more times. Relax.

COMMENTS
If you do this kriya for 40 days you can rebuild the molecular structure of the body. This meditation must not be done for more than 9 minutes total.

CHAPTER TEN

TRANSITIONS: REBIRTHING, LIVING & DYING

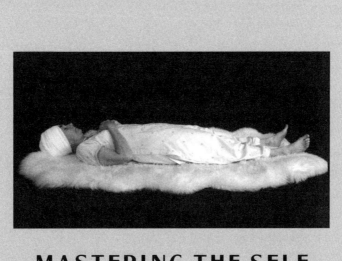

MASTERING THE SELF

Living with Exalted Consciousness

"Time changes, the man changes, the environment changes, the need changes, change is inevitable. There is no way to get out of it, because change is a part of being. There will be change and, actually, there should be change."

–Yogi Bhajan

How we die says a lot about how we lived. "It is a good day to die" was the rallying cry of Native Americans as they went into battle—warriors to the end. Can we say the same? Are we spiritually fit, today, to make that transition? What about the other transitions we have to make, at every age and stage of our life? Do we welcome old age and maturity or shun it? Do we cling to youth, as it seems the entire culture around us does, or do we embrace the fruits of maturity and everything that comes with it? Our capacity as practitioners to transition through these critical moments in our lives is the test of our spiritual maturity and our identity.

"Time changes, the man changes, the environment changes, the need changes, change is inevitable. There is no way to get out of it, because change is a part of being. There will be change and, actually, there should be change. There is no problem as far as change is concerned; but with every change in our life, one thing doesn't change. We don't change our attachment to our own ego—that never changes.

"Just consider this proposition. Your ego, on which you are basing your future, does not change; while in actual reality, you are changing. So you are changing, but your ego is stationary. What does that mean? You are not on the point and you are not where you should be; the result is very evident—unhappiness.

"Vyas, the most beautiful, learned man ever to exist on this planet was asked: "Lord Vyas, there is no scripture which is not known to you, there is no knowledge which you do not know. Could you tell us, What is most difficult for a man?"

He said, "It is very simple. The only difficult thing with a man is that he does not change his ego and consider the reality."

"So, everyday of your life, every stage of your life, demands a change in you. Every new sidewalk, movement, friendship, and personality, demands a change in you. Every idea, every thought demands a change in you. Change is your real happiness, and you are the ones who resist change! We resist change, why? Because we are hung up on habits and the totality of our habits is the ego."

–Yogi Bhajan, October 22, 1971

Our attachment to ego limits us when our True Identity is limitless, deathless, beyond fear, and beyond death. This path gives us countless examples of deathlessness—*akal*; dead yet alive—*jivan mukt*; courage in the face of insurmountable odds; and resilience under the most trying conditions. The sons of Guru Gobind Singh, the life and death of Guru Arjan, the 40-Liberated Ones, the list goes on. This is the path of the spiritual warrior; the one who is willing to serve, even as they lose their life. Because even though most of us don't want to admit it, death is our greatest fear. We must conquer our fears in order to live as Raj Yogis.

"If you want to play the game of love, put your head on the palm of your hand and walk this path. Now you are entering a society of the headless. There is no other clear, clean, or honest directive than this: if you want to walk on this path, if you want to put your foot on this path, then don't hesitate to give your head... this path is fearless—undaunted—without logic, reason or earthly mind. We offer ourself today to God and Guru. If death comes, we will dance and play the song of death with it as equals. . . . Remember: it is the impossible, which is made possible, and that is called the exalted consciousness of the individual."

–Yogi Bhajan, April 17, 1977

These kriyas and meditations break the bonds that keep you tied to this earthly plane, strengthen your resolve and your identity as you pass through the various stages of life—youth, maturity, and the wisdom years—and give you the tools you need to cross the inevitable hour of death. At that hour, we become the arbiters of our own lives; we choose. Begin choosing now. Change now. Transform now. Forgive now. Wake up, today, so that your tomorrow can be bright and bountiful and beautiful.

Living Weightlessly:
Breaking the Bonds of Earth

1. Sit in Easy Pose. Interlace the fingers so that the tips of the fingers don't quite meet the webbing of the opposite hand. The thumbs are open and pointing up. Press this mudra into the diaphragm on each exhale. Suck in the breath powerfully through firm round lips and turn to the left. Exhale center. Inhale center and turn the head to the right. Exhale center and continue. **6 minutes.**

2. Release the mudra and begin Breath of Fire through the mouth. Use the cheeks and the diaphragm. Let the checks puff out with the breath. Heavy breath. **4 1/2 minutes.**

Dying is nothing; it's just like a balloon leaving the earth and moving toward the heavens.

3. Transition into Baby Pose. Sitting on the heels, bring the forehead to the ground, arms at the sides, palms facing up. If possible, play the gong. **15 minutes.**

Enjoy it. It's very beautiful. You don't have to hustle. Release the breath. The body relaxes totally and completely. It's just letting the balloon leave the earth. Get into weightlessness. Totally disconnect with the body. Some of you will feel tremendous pressure on the forehead; others will be able to let it go. Different bodies will have different experiences. But if you totally relax and let it go; you will let it go. Find your state of innocence. No karmic weight. State of weightlessness. No reality and non-reality; in this neutral state, resurrect toward the heavens. Let it go. Resurrect! Rise! Like angels of light toward the heavens. Transparent.

Confront death with the sharpest, most powerful, radiant light. Penetrate through the valley of darkness. Penetrate through the valley of darkness. Penetrate through the valley of darkness. Penetrate through the valley of darkness. Confront death and win. Confront sorrows and loss. Resurrect to your height. Let it go. Let it go. Feel alive. Newborn. Arise praising the Lord, your God in experience. Be born. [Dhan Dhan Ram Das Gur recording by Sangeet Kaur [entitled "Naad"] is used in class; gong continues] Cross the hour of the past into the valley of the newness. Feel the newness of your body.

Living Weightlessly:
Breaking the Bonds of Earth

4. Come sitting up. Concentrate at the Heart Center, and sing. **11 minutes**.

Arise smiling and chanting and singing. Open up. Concentrate on the heart center and open up. Enjoy the newness. Spread high the frequency of joy—high frequency of joy. Uplift the feelings. Sophisticate them. Enter the realm of celestial self. Vibrate.

TO END: Inhale deep. Suspend for **30-40 seconds**. Exhale. 3 times. Feel light. Let it go. All the disease. All the karma. All the unwantedness. Let it go. Let it go. Relax. Relax. Relax.

5. Meditate in silence listening to music.

In class, the following songs were played: Death is the Sacred Alter by Livtar Singh; followed by Walking up the Mountain by Gurudass Singh and Krishna Kaur; followed by I Have My God with Me by Krishna Kaur.

COMMENTS

Yogi Bhajan led this meditation as a guided visualization. If you are practicing this meditation on your own, record the visualization in your own voice, guiding your own journey and breaking your own bonds. If teaching this kriya in class and you do not have a gong, use a recording, as you guide your students through the visualization. The gong is an essential element to this kriya, the sound of the *adi nath*, which facilitates the soul's breaking away from its earthly bonds.

From Womb to Birth

PART ONE

Sit comfortably in a meditative pose. Let your breath become light and meditative. *(Play the Narayan Shabd in the background if you wish.)* Imagine that you are in a deep self-hypnosis; you are just pure soul. A light guided by your spirit, God, and your teachers. You feel the pull of earth and life. You intuitively sense the life you are offered and choose it fully. You accept all its challenges and lessons, all the chances to complete karmas, all the blessings to reach and elevate others.

Then you slip into the watery world of the womb in a small body, fed by the navel point and you begin to move and sense. You are intuitively sensitive. Without words you feel and know through vibration.

Allow yourself to get into the womb of the mother. Look at the world around you. See the whole world through the skin of the belly. With unlimited telescopic vision survey this life you will enter and the world around you. Hear all the sounds and feel the feelings of the mother like waves in the water as you float.

Now see through the eyes of the mother. Give the mother a thought: "This soul, blessed being, is coming to bless the world. This soul will be itself, supported by my prayer and by the love of the entire universe." Then imagine using your mental power as a mother to see the world through the child's eyes. See what it is this child will get into. Penetrate and concentrate so the child is aware and ready to engage the world. So that with the first breath there is nothing but gratitude and trust. In that innocence the entire world will serve that child and all will come to that child like a magnet. The destiny will run to this child like a magnet. Prepare the child with love and a vision to be ready for this world and its opportunities. Life is for a purpose. Life is to enjoy the beauty, the bounty and the bliss of the soul. When we feel this and recognize the environments we face, the environments and people serve us in our destiny.

Meditate this way, communicate to that child for **11 minutes**. Then prepare for birth as you feel the time approach.

From Womb to Birth

PART TWO

1. Sit erect and alert. Extend the arms forward, parallel to the ground. Make fists keeping the index finger extended. Open your mouth wide. Lock the tongue down at the base of the lower front teeth. Begin to breathe through the mouth with a long, deep, consciousness breath. Make the breath equal in and out, using the Navel Point. Pump the Navel Point in on the exhale. Get a steady rhythm going. Reduce yourself to a point in the navel. Gradually focus at the navel and relive the experience of birth. Keep the eyes closed. Build up to the birth and the first breath. Imagine that first breath as open, powerful, permission-giving, energizing, and flowing into every cell.
5-11 minutes.

2. Then relax your hands into your lap. Keep the eyes closed. Begin to chant, **Ham dam har har har har ham dam** as you pump the navel.
Continue for **5 minutes.**
TO END: Inhale through the nose as you guide the energy up your spine, vertebrae by vertebrae. Then exhale completely. Repeat this **3-11 times.** Then talk to your neighbors and walk around for **5 minutes.**

3. Place the left hand in front of the Heart Center. Fingers point forward parallel to the ground with the palm facing to the right. Keep the thumb extended upward. Bring the right ring and middle fingertips into the center of the left palm. The right palm will be facing the chest. The right thumb is extended and pointing up. Look down past the tip of the nose. Chant *Har* continuously. (*Tantric Har* recording can be used.)
Continue up to **31 minutes.**

To consolidate the effects, do this for 90 days, it will make the change consistent for the rest of your life. This will balance and open all the chakras. It moves the energy up from the navel to the heart, throat and third eye. Then it goes back down and circulates again. The first breath is cleared and that balanced prana is taken through all the chakras.

see comments on next page

TRANSITIONS
From Womb to Birth

COMMENTS

The two most crucial breaths you take are your first, at birth, and your last, at death. Technically speaking, you live for as long as a breath. There is no future—only the length of this breath.

The first breath is special. It sets the quality and tone of the prana for your life. If this first breath is open, free and fearless, life will be projective, attractive and consciously happy. If we come to that first breath filled with fear, internal conflicts from the mother's projections or rejection of the world and not accepting of this birth, then we prevent ourselves from feeling the happiness in our life. It doesn't matter how hard or easy the life will be—happiness is a birthright, like the breath. When we can embrace each moment and feel the reality of the soul and project it with a relaxed mind, we know happiness.

This meditation links you back to that first breath. It adjusts the pattern of your life force. It helps you connect to your innate ecstasy and ability to call on all of nature to give you what you need. It gives a deep security to every cell. Adjust the imprint of this first breath and every breath thereafter becomes more vital, flowing and creative.

Meditation for Shakti Pad
& Midlife Transition

Sit in Easy Pose.

MUDRA: Extend the first two fingers of the left hand and the index finger of the right hand. Touch them together at the tips to form and upside down "V" pointing up. The remaining fingers are bent and joined with the fingers of the other hand from the first to second joint. Thumb tips meet and point toward the body. With the elbows bent, bring the hands up and in until they meet just below the level of the throat.

EYES: Eyes are closed.

MANTRA: Chant in a monotone the following mantra:

Ardaas Bhayee, Amar Daas Guroo
Amar Daas Guroo, Ardaas Bhayee
Raam Daas Guroo, Raam Daas Guroo
Raam Daas Guroo, Sachee Sahee

The prayer is offered, oh Guru Amar Das
Guru Amar Das, the prayer is offered.
Guru Ram Das, Guru Ram Das
Guru Ram Das, it is truly sealed.

TIME: **11 minutes**.

COMMENTS

This is a three-way energy. This mantra will help people who are going through Shakti Pad. If a man cannot relax himself voluntarily, cannot communicate voluntarily, cannot understand himself voluntarily, and cannot project within, the outside world becomes nothing but a misery.

Guided Meditation with the Master to Enter the Fall & Winter Season

Sit straight in Easy Pose.

MUDRA: Bring the hands a few inches in front of the Heart Center, with the fingertips touching and the palms spread. The fingertips point up to the sky and the thumbs reach back toward the torso. "Try to see how the energy moves. You will feel the reality of the body."

This is a guided meditation. Listen to Yogi Bhajan recite the following meditation or record the entire script in your own voice and do the meditation in that way.

"Inhale deep and ride on the breath, in and out, long and deep, as honestly as you can. Take the inner being in this body, simply by meditative force. Do not try to understand that you cannot do it. It is not difficult, but it is a great experience. Pull your mental body out of your body. Just take it out. Just simply coordinate between you, your environments, your activities and your own preciousness.

Your mental body, when you command it, is very pure, very clear. And it is yours. It is not related to the physical activities, although the mental body is with you. Things are corrupt only when you are in your physical body and your mental body is not combined. So, do coordinate—you have that power—and take this out, out of your being. Time is with us, the wind is behind us, and virtuous we are.

It's a very special Saturday; therefore the Saturn energy in the penetrating form of its being is passing through, irrespective of any force or any effort. That's why I chose it and we have a time window only. So this breath has to be very long and down to the Navel Point. Inhale deeply and hold and exhale completely out.

The power which we have is our virtue. Our virtue is extremely powerful. Our value is humongous. Value, we give! Virtues, we experience! Our values are our values. The majority of the time we forget that we have values. But most of the time, if we practice these things, we remember our values. Once a person follows one's own values, that is all Divinity is about.

So keep the breath long, deep and evaluate yourself. Give yourself values. The first value you can give yourself is, 'I am virtuous, I am beautiful, God created me in the best form. Thank God I've been given health, happiness, and wealth.' You know, you are a wonder of the world. Recognize the fact. Concentrate on these things.

Now comes the Shintoism, the Japanese faith. See that you are just a blade of grass, beautiful, green and you are covering your values. Start covering your values as a blade of grass, with an extreme sense of self-cooperation. The tips of the fingers must meet so that circulation can coordinate the two parts of the body, and your valuable and virtuous and wonderful body is right at this time under manual control. Your

Guided Meditation with the Master to Enter the Fall & Winter Season

mental body is taken out. The mental body is looking at your physical body as you are sitting. Practice this split. Once you can separate your mental body and practice separating it, as we keep on doing, there is no problem—at the time of death you can split your mental body and be free of karma. You will never have a rebirth again. That is guaranteed.

This is your reality: You have physical body, you have a mental body, and you have a body of bliss. When you separate that, in-between you watch over this body, see how beautiful it is?

The breath has to be very long and deep because your spiritual body, your physical body, your mental body and your being are separate. You have never been taught this. You have never been told. You think you are one bundle. Feel the super and extreme contentment. That will bring you prosperity. Ride on your breath and just feel supremely contented. That will give you the prosperity which you are looking for. It's no use living rich, it's no use living poor, it's no use being great if you cannot demonstrate to yourself that you can separate your bodies and you can separate that strength. And you cannot only visualize it, but experience it. In this experience, you are the Supreme.

Every religion goes round and round and round and speaks of only one thing—consciousness of the Self. Consciousness of the Self is just a phrase to us. But let us consider what consciousness of the Self is: When we know we have a spiritual body, we have a mental body, we have a physical body.

Your mental body and your radiant body—have you ever put them together? They are yours. Nobody will know it; but you will be charged and recharged with the energy. What is more beautiful in this Earth than you? What is more pure and shining than you? What is more cool and calm and quiet than you? In the eyes of God you are everything.

Take a long deep breath and ride on it. Fortune and misfortune are two wavelengths. By your self-hypnosis, you can put your body on any wavelength you need. In the common man's language we call it reputation.

The body's membranes and the body's adjustment and the body's main nervous system are going to adjust now. You are within that time, therefore, please breathe long and deep and cure yourself forever. Heal! Take long, deep breaths and ride on it and keep your mental body away. See only where the tips of the fingers meet.

Circulate your breath. Keep the mental body separate. Concentrate on the physical body, in the realm of personal consciousness. You are beautiful, you are bountiful, you are blissful, you are virtuous, you have vigor, self-control. Apply all that!

The central nerve in the Navel Point can be touched by a deep breath. A split mental body can give you a vast area of coexistence. All your five channels and *tattvas* are totally balanced at the moment. Your Arcline is clear. Can you believe the little bit that we have done? It is ridiculous that we suffer here, there and everywhere. What for? America needs peace; it needs love; it needs tons of smiles. It needs us—"we the people."

The rotation of the planet will change the energy and it will change everything. Now is the time. Breathe long and deep. Get it when it is available. Bring in you the coziness. Colorful coziness. Split the light inside. Bring in the special breath of life. If you know how to concentrate, meditate and breathe, this is the time.

Breathe in deep and hold it tight, hold it tight, breathe out. Breathe in, hold it, now breathe out. Breathe in all the virtues of God and breathe out peace for the world. Breathe in long and deep, hold it, love it, feel it and then let it go. Now put all the pressure on the fingertips. Inhale deep. Put a tight trip on the fingers. Let it go. Inhale deep. Make the fingers very tight. Feel the purpose of life and prosperity. Let it go. That's it,

Inhale deeply, exhale and relax."

Naraa Kar Kriya: Crossing the Crisis

Bring the hands into Gyan Mudra, each thumb locking the fingernail of the forefinger down forcefully. The three remaining fingers remain straight and together. Link the Gyan Mudras with each other. Bring the elbows close to the body so that the locked mudras are held in the space between the Heart Center and the throat. The palms are open, facing forward. Pull the locks against each other so that there is tremendous pressure on the forefingers.

EYES: Eyes are focused at the tip of the nose, or at the Third Eye Point with eyes closed—individual choice.

MANTRA: Maintaining the mudra throughout:

Sing along with the Shabd: *Bhand Jamee-ai*. **5 minutes**.

Sing along with the Shabd: *Dhan Dhan Ram Das Gur*. Recording by Sangeet Kaur (entitled "*Naad*") was used in class. **11 minutes**.
Imagine the Golden Temple.

Sing along with Shabd: *Ab Jan Upar*. **7 minutes**.
Chant the mantra powerfully.

(See Appendix, pages 176-178 for the Shabd Sheets.)

COMMENTS

"Bring God on Earth, let the heavens give the way. Adi Shakti must prevail. Penetrate, penetrate, cut the shield. Penetrate, penetrate, penetrate, cut the shield.

There is nothing you can get without giving—balance. You have to make a sacrifice to achieve. Every victory has a price, every defeat has a pain, therefore don't let your ego play an unnecessary role. The best is to accept the Will of God, and the Will of God is what is best for all, not what is best for you. That is the only difference. . . . If you sacrifice your will over divine will, then you wish good for all and you shall be the best, that is the way to cross the crisis."

Meditation for Maturity

Sit in Easy Pose.

MUDRA & MOVEMENT: The right hand grasps the left thumb, then fold the left fingers over the back of the right hand. Place them at the solar plexus. Pull the navel in at least 3 inches with each beat of the mantra.

MANTRA: Recording by Ragi Jagjit Singh, *Sat Nam Wahe Guru Version #2* is used.

Sat Naam Sat Naam
Whaa-hay Guroo Whaa-hay Guroo
Truth is my Identity.
Ecstasy of the Eternal Wisdom.

TIME: Approximately **22 minutes**.

TO END: Inhale deeply and press hard. Squeeze the entire body. Balance the Navel Point. Fire out with Cannon Breath. Do this 2 more times.

TRANSITIONS
Crossing the Hour of Death

1. Sit in Easy Pose. The right hand and left hand cross at a 45 degree angle. The fingers of the right hand rest on the left hand, making an X. This is placed four to six inches from the face. Breathe a Long Deep Breath, making the breath harder and harder. Begin by looking in your hands and relating to the breath. Then, roll the eyes up toward the brow point, and feel the breath. Breathe from the lower ribs. **5 1/2 minutes**.

That is the sign, called crossing the hour. When you are hit by that moment, systematically the breath becomes hard. It is called solid breath. You start breathing by the lower ribs. It means the lower lungs start becoming inflated.

2. Maintain the mudra and breathe through the mouth. Breathe very hard; make an effort. Close your eyes totally. Concentrate on letting the soul go from the top of the skull. Make the breath harder and harder. **3 1/2 minutes**.

Practice this breath when you are alive and well.

3. Release the breath and slowly fall down onto your back. Hands rest at the Heart Center. Start going deeper and deeper, releasing your physical body and your awareness. Consciously pass out. Start sinking and start dying. **30 minutes**.

Play a beautiful version of Sat Nam Wahe Guru. Yogi Bhajan began playing the gong about 10 minutes into the posture.

"A dead man has no choice what ground he gets. It is called dying in consciousness. Practically prepare yourself for death. Go deeper and touch the center of the earth. Lose conscious control of your physical body. Sink into death as if you were being carried down by an elevator. Leave mental control and conscious control of the physical existence. Down deep in your heart let it go. Let it go. Let the thought go. You are going home. Thoughts are the quality of the earth; relate to no thought. Think only that you are being carried down in a cylindrical lift and being carried into a vast area of bright light. Light is brighter and depth is deeper; visualize a deep place where you see nothing but dazzling bright light. Now visualize two sides: one is warm and cozy; the other is very icy and cold. Start walking toward the dazzling icy pathway, a winding pathway going through the hills, an absolutely dazzling light and snowy atmosphere. Dazzling snowy pathway is the pathway to the heavens; start moving through it, passing through the winding, dazzling path, freezing, snowy, windy path. Keep going; don't stop. Feel no physical senses or contact, move as a transparent body. You are transparent body in the beginning; transform yourself into a transparent body now. Go through the penetrating body and walk through this valley of dazzling light, leaving behind the coziness of senses. Leave behind the coziness of senses. Let it go. Let the opaqueness go."

Crossing the Hour of Death

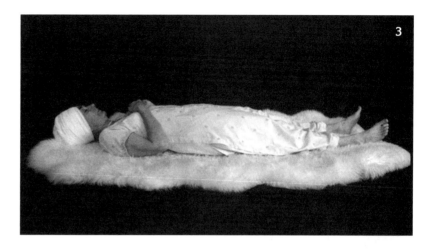

4. Sit in Easy Pose. Meditate with the music. The gong continues.
12 minutes.

TO END: Inhale Deep. Hold for **40 seconds.** Exhale. Do this 3 times.
Inhale deeply. Hold for **1 minute**. Exhale. Inhale deeply. Hold for **30
seconds**. Relax.

*Coordinate your senses and resurrect. Lift up your physical form. Be here now.
Active and valid. Merge with the chanting. Now penetrate your sound with the
sound of the gong; listen to that sound as the power of your prayer. Elevate
yourself. Power of the shabd and power of the divine sound are going to contrast;
penetrate with your strength.*

Meditation to Go Through Death into the Higher Levels of Ether

Sit in Easy Pose with a straight spine.

MUDRA: Place the hands in Prayer Pose. Pull the thumbs back and separate them like the horns of a ram's head. Press the hands together and keep the thumbs wide apart. Hold the hand position in front of the Heart Center, with the fingers pointing forward. The elbows are tucked into the sides.

EYES: Eyes are focused at the tip of the nose.

BREATH: Deeply inhale and completely exhale as the mantra is chanted in a monotone (one repetition is 4 seconds).

MANTRA:

Haree Haree Haree Haree Haree Haree Haree Har

TIME: Best done before bedtime for **31 minutes.**

COMMENTS

This meditation builds your circumvent field strength. It is a very technical, subtle, powerful and beautiful meditation. It will make you happy if you can do it. It takes care of physical and mental imbalance.

It is a circumvent meditation which takes care of your problems in the world hereafter. The thumbs represent the ego and the central part of the brain. The meditation is effective because of the ego split of the thumbs.

The mantra uses two qualities of the seed word *Har*. *Har* is Creative Infinity, *Haree* is that Creative Infinity in its completion; it's fulfillment.

SHABD SHEETS

Bhand Jamee-ai

In Praise of Woman • Guru Nanak, Siri Guru Granth Sahib, page 473

Bhand jamee-ai bhand nimee-ai	*From woman, man is born, within woman, man is conceived.*
Bhand mangan vee-aaho.	*To woman he is engaged and married.*
Bhandho hovai dostee	*Woman becomes his friend.*
Bhandho chalai raaho	*Through woman, the future generations come.*
Bhandh muaa bhandh bhaalee-ai	*When his woman dies, he seeks another woman.*
Bhandh hovai bandhaan	*To woman he is bound.*
So keo manndaa aakhee-ai	*So why call her bad?*
Jit jameh raajaan	*From her, kings are born.*
Bhandho hee bhandh oopajai	*From woman, woman is born.*
Bhandhai baajh na ko-eh	*Without woman, there would be no one at all.*
Naanak bhandhai baaharaa	*O, Nanak! The only one without a woman*
Ayko sachaa so-eh	*is the One True Lord.*
Jit mukh sadaa saalaahe-ai	*That mouth which continually praises the Lord*
Bhaagaa ratee chaar.	*is blessed and beautiful.*
Naanak tay mukh oojalay	*O Nanak! Their faces shall be radiant*
tit sachai darbaa-eh	*in the Court of the True Lord.*

ਭੰਡਿ ਜੰਮੀਐ ਭੰਡਿ ਨਿੰਮੀਐ ਭੰਡਿ ਮੰਗਣੁ ਵੀਆਹੁ

ਭੰਡਹੁ ਹੋਵੈ ਦੋਸਤੀ ਭੰਡਹੁ ਚਲੈ ਰਾਹੁ

ਭੰਡੁ ਮੁਆ ਭੰਡੁ ਭਾਲੀਐ ਭੰਡਿ ਹੋਵੈ ਬੰਧਾਨੁ

ਸੋ ਕਿਉ ਮੰਦਾ ਆਖੀਐ ਜਿਤੁ ਜੰਮਹਿ ਰਾਜਾਨ

ਭੰਡਹੁ ਹੀ ਭੰਡੁ ਉਪਜੈ ਭੰਡੈ ਬਾਝੁ ਨ ਕੋਇ

ਨਾਨਕ ਭੰਡੈ ਬਾਹਰਾ ਏਕੋ ਸਚਾ ਸੋਇ

ਜਿਤੁ ਮੁਖਿ ਸਦਾ ਸਾਲਾਹੀਐ ਭਾਗਾ ਰਤੀ ਚਾਰਿ

ਨਾਨਕ ਤੇ ਮੁਖ ਉਜਲੇ ਤਿਤੁ ਸਚੈ ਦਰਬਾਰਿ

Dhan Dhan Ram Das Gur

In Praise of Guru Ram Das • Siri Guru Granth Sahib, page 968

Dhan Dhan Ram Das Gur	*Praise, Praise Guru Ram Das!*
Jin siri-aa- tinai savaari-aa	*The Creator has adorned & embellished you!*
Pooree ho-ee karaamaat	*Perfect is the Miracle of your making*
Aap sirjanhaarai dhaari-aa	*The Creator has installed you on the Throne*
Sikhee atai sangatee	*Your Sikhs, and all people of consciousness bow*
Paarbrahm kar namasakaari-aa	*And revere you as a being of supreme consciousness*
Atal athaaho atoll too(n)	*You are unshakeable, unfathomable,immeasurable*
Tayraa ant na paaraavaari-aa	*Your extent is beyond all limits*
Jinee too(n) sayvi-aa bhaa-u kar	*Those who serve you with love*
Say tudh paar utaari-aa	*Are carried across the world-ocean by you*
Lab lobh kaam krodh moho	*The five passions of greed,attachment,lust, anger*
Maar kadhay tudh saparvaari-aa	*And ego have been transformed by you*
Dhaan so tayraa thaan hai	*Great and praised is your Realm*
Sach tayraa paisakaari-aa	*Truest of the true are Your bounties*
Nanak too(n) lehnaa too(n) hai	*You are Nanak, you are Angad,*
Gur Amar too(n) veechaari-aa	*And Guru Amar Das; I recognize this in you*
Gur dithaa taan man saadhaari-aa	*Seeing the Guru, my soul is comforted!*

ਧੰਨੁ ਧੰਨੁ ਰਾਮਦਾਸ ਗੁਰੁ ਜਿਨਿ ਸਿਰਿਆ ਤਿਨੈ ਸਵਾਰਿਆ
ਪੂਰੀ ਹੋਈ ਕਰਾਮਾਤਿ ਆਪਿ ਸਿਰਜਣਹਾਰੈ ਧਾਰਿਆ
ਸਿਖੀ ਅਤੈ ਸੰਗਤੀ ਪਾਰਬ੍ਰਹਮੁ ਕਰਿ ਨਮਸਕਾਰਿਆ
ਅਟਲੁ ਅਥਾਹੁ ਅਤੋਲੁ ਤੂ ਤੇਰਾ ਅੰਤੁ ਨ ਪਾਰਾਵਾਰਿਆ
ਜਿਨੀ ਤੂੰ ਸੇਵਿਆ ਭਾਉ ਕਰਿ ਸੇ ਤੁਧੁ ਪਾਰਿ ਉਤਾਰਿਆ
ਲਬੁ ਲੋਭੁ ਕਾਮੁ ਕਰੋਧੁ ਮੋਹੁ ਮਾਰਿ ਕਢੇ ਤੁਧੁ ਸਪਰਵਾਰਿਆ
ਧੰਨੁ ਸੁ ਤੇਰਾ ਥਾਨੁ ਹੈ ਸਚੁ ਤੇਰਾ ਪੈਸਕਾਰਿਆ
ਨਾਨਕੁ ਤੂ ਲਹਣਾ ਤੂ ਹੈ ਗੁਰੁ ਅਮਰੁ ਤੂ ਵੀਚਾਰਿਆ
ਗੁਰੁ ਡਿਠਾ ਤਾਂ ਮਨੁ ਸਾਧਾਰਿਆ

178

Ab Jan Upar

Guru Arjun Dev • Siri Guru Granth Sahib, page 1217

Ab jan upar ko na pukareh
Pookaaran kau jo udam kartaa
Gur parmaysar taa kau maarai
Nirvairai sang vair rachaavai
Har dargeh oh-ho haarai
Aad jugaad prabh kee vadh-aa-ee

Jan kee paij savaarai
Nirbhau bhay sagal bhau mithiaa
Charn kamal aadhaarai
Gur kai bachan japio naa-au
Naanak pargat bhaeeau sansaarai

Now, no one complains about the Lord's humble servant.
Whoever tries to complain is destroyed by the Guru,
the Transcendent Lord God. || 1 || Pause ||
Whoever harbors vengeance against the One who is beyond
all vengenace, shall lose in the Court of the Lord.
From the very beginning of time, and throughout the ages,
it is the glorious greatness of God
That He preserves the honor of His humble servants. || 1 ||
The mortal becomes fearless, and all his fears are taken away,
When he leans on the Support of the Lord's Lotus Feet.
Chanting the Name, through the Guru's Word,
Nanak has become famous throughout the world.

ਅਬ ਜਨ ਉਪਰਿ ਕੋ ਨ ਪੁਕਾਰੈ
ਪੁਕਾਰਨ ਕਉ ਜੋ ਉਦਮੁ ਕਰਤਾ
ਗੁਰੁ ਪਰਮੇਸਰੁ ਤਾ ਕਉ ਮਾਰੈ
ਨਿਰਵੈਰੈ ਸੰਗਿ ਵੈਰੁ ਰਚਾਵੈ
ਹਰਿ ਦਰਗਹ ਓਹੁ ਹਾਰੈ
ਆਦਿ ਜੁਗਾਦਿ ਪ੍ਰਭ ਕੀ ਵਡਿਆਈ
ਜਨ ਕੀ ਪੈਜ ਸਵਾਰੈ
ਨਿਰਭਉ ਭਏ ਸਗਲ ਭਉ ਮਿਟਿਆ
ਚਰਨ ਕਮਲ ਆਧਾਰੈ
ਗੁਰ ਕੈ ਬਚਨਿ ਜਪਿਓ ਨਾਉ
ਨਾਨਕ ਪ੍ਰਗਟ ਭਇਓ ਸੰਸਾਰੈ

GLOSSARY

If you are a Kundalini Yogi, you may be familiar with many of the yoga terms used throughout this manual. If you haven't yet studied Kundalini Yoga as taught by Yogi Bhajan®, here is a brief introduction to terms. For best results in your practice, we encourage you to study with a KRI certified Kundalini Yoga teacher in your local community.

Adi Shakti: Literally means "Primal Power." Adi means "primal" or "first" and Shakti means "God's power manifested." The Adi Shakti has been worshipped for centuries in the Orient in the form of the goddess, and thus the female energy of Infinity is also referred to as Adi Shakti. Woman is seen as a manifestation of the Adi Shakti energy.

Age of Aquarius: The next in a succession of astrological ages each lasting roughly 2,000 years. Fully inaugurated in ad 2012, the Aquarian Age will witness a radical change in consciousness, human sensitivity, and technology. The central change of this new age emphasizes an increased sensitivity and evolution of our power of awareness and a new relationship to our mind.

Amrit Vela: Literally "ambrosial time." It is the 2-1/2 hours before the rising of the sun. During this special time you are most receptive to the soul; you can clear the subconscious of wrong habits and impulses; and you can connect with the teachers and saints from all traditions. It is the best time to perform sadhana (spiritual discipline).

Ang Sang Wahe Guru: "God exists in every part of me."

Aradhana: The second stage of spiritual discipline: sadhana, aradhana, prabhupati.

Arcline: One of 10 bodies of a human being. It is a thin bright arc, like a halo, that goes from ear to ear over the forehead near the normal hairline. It reflects the interaction of the soul of the person with its vital energy resources, and in it are written the potential, destiny, and health of the person. Women have a second Arcline from nipple to nipple.

Ardas: Prayer; the traditional formal prayer of the Sikhs.

Asana: Position, seat, yogic posture.

Ashram: A learning center for spiritual growth.

Ashtang Mantra: Most Kundalini Yoga Mantras are Ashtang Mantras, meaning they have 8 beats or 8 component parts in the sound current.

Aura: One of the 10 bodies, the aura is the radiant field of energy and consciousness that surrounds the physical body and which holds and organizes the seven centers of energy called chakras. Its strength, measured by brightness and radius, determines the vitality and integrity of a person.

Bana: Clothing which projects a particular consciousness.

Bani: Speech which projects a particular, elevated consciousness. Literally 'word'; refers to the Word of God contained in the Sikh Sacred writings.

Banis: The Sikh daily prayers.

Bhagvati (or Bhagauti): Creative Power of the Universe.

Bhakti: Self-purification. The devotional form of yoga.

Bandh: A body lock. There are three which make up the Maha Bandh or Great Lock: Jalandhar Bandh, Udiyana Bandh and Mulbandh.

Breath of Fire: One of the foundational breath techniques used in the practice of Kundalini Yoga. It accompanies many postures, and has numerous beneficial effects. It is important to master this breath so that it is done accurately and becomes automatic. See page 152 for detailed instructions.

Chakra: The word connotes a wheel in action. It usually refers to the seven primary energy centers in the aura that align along the spine from the base to the top of the skull. Each chakra is a center of consciousness with a set of values, concerns, and powers of action associated with it.

Cherdi Kala. In high spirits. In the context of yoga, it refers literally to the moment when the Crown Chakra opens, the kundalini awakens, and you experience an expansion of spirit and a love for all brotherhood and sisterhood.

Dharma: A path of righteous living.

Easy Pose: This is a simple but stable yogic sitting posture. It is sitting cross-legged "tailor fashion," but with a yogic awareness of keeping the spine straight, with the lower spine slightly forward so the upper spine can stay straight.

Gatka: Indian martial art of sword fighting. Also refers to the use of mantra to cut through negativity or inertia and change the direction of the thought.

Golden Chain of Teachers or the Golden Link: Historically it is the long line of spiritual masters who have preceded us. Practically it is the subtle link between the consciousness of a student and the master, which has the power to guide and protect the energy of a teaching and its techniques. This link requires the student to put aside the ego and limitations and act in complete synchrony or devotion to the highest consciousness of the master and the teachings.

Gunas: The three conditions of matter: Satva (satvaa)—pure essence (saintliness), rajas (raajaas)—active, creative or initiating energy (imperial), and tamas (taamaas)—inertia or decay.

Gurbani: Word of the Guru. Refers particularly to the words from the Siri Guru Granth Sahib.

Gurmukh: Literally, one whose face is always turned toward the Guru, or one whose mouth always repeats the Guru's words; a perfectly devoted person.

Guru Mantra: Wahe Guru is the Guru Mantra in the Sikh Tradition. Refers to the bij or seed mantra given from teacher to student to elevate the consciousness.

Gyan Mudra: The most commonly used mudra for meditation. The tip of the thumb touches the tip of the Jupiter (index) finger. This stimulates knowledge, wisdom, and the power to compute. The energy of the index finger is associated with Jupiter, representing expansion. Its qualities are receptivity and calm.

Hukam: An order from the Guru.

Ida: One of the three major channels (nadis) for subtle energy in the body. It is associated with the flow of breath through the left nostril and represents the qualities of the moon—calmness, receptivity, coolness, and imagination. It is associated with the functions of the parasympathetic nervous system but is not identical to it nor derived from it.

I

shnan (ishnaan): A system of water therapy referred to in the West as "hydrotherapy", involving bathing in cold water to open the capillaries and flush the system, thus increasing the circulation and tonifying the glands and general health of the body.

Jaap Sahib: A prayer written by Guru Gobind Singh which gives one conscious awareness of one's grace; one of the banis, or daily prayer of the Sikhs.

Jalandar Bandh also called Neck Lock: This is the most basic of the locks. It is a general rule to apply it in all chanting meditations and during most pranayams. Whenever you are holding the breath in or out, it is usually applied unless instructed otherwise. Sit comfortably with the spine straight. Lift the chest and sternum upward. Gently stretch the back of the neck straight by pulling the chin toward the back of the neck. The head stays level and centered, and does not tilt forward or to either side. The muscles of the neck and throat remain loose. Keep the muscles of the face and brow relaxed.

Japji Sahib: An inspired poem, or scripture composed by Guru Nanak. *Japji Sahib* provides a view of the cosmos, the soul, the mind, the challenge of life, and describes the impact of our actions. Its 40 stanzas are thea source of many mantras and can be used as a whole or in part to guide both your mind and your heart.

Japa: Literally "to repeat." It is the conscious, alert, and precise repetition of a mantra.

Ji: Literally meaning "soul," used as a term of endearment or sign of respect.

Kakars (the 5Ks): The five symbols worn by baptized Sikhs: Kesh, Kirpan, Katcheras, Kanga and Kara. Uncut hair, small, single-edged sword, special cotton underwear, wooden comb and steel bracelet, respectively.

Khalsa: Traditionally and literally it means "Pure One." In this path it refers to a pure state of consciousness and lifestyle, that sees the purity in all.

Kriya: Literally means "completed action." An integrated sequence of postures, breath, and sound that work together to manifest a particular state. Kundalini Yoga as taught by Yogi Bhajan® is structured in kriyas, a sequence of postures and yoga techniques used to produce a particular impact on the psyche, body, or self. The structure of each kriya has been designed to generate, organize, and deliver a particular state or change of state, thereby completing a cycle of effect.

Kundalini: Comes from the word "Kundal," curled hair; coiled energy; the creative potential of an individual.

Kundalini Yoga: A Raj Yoga that creates vitality in the body, balance in the mind, and openness to the spirit. It is used by the householder, busy in the world, to create immediate clarity. The fourth Guru in the Sikh tradition, Guru Ram Das, was acknowledged as the greatest Raj Yogi. He opened this long-secret tradition to all.

Langar: Free kitchen associated with Sikh worship service.

Long Deep Breathing: One of the most basic yogic breaths. It uses the full capacity of the lungs. Long Deep Breathing starts by filling the abdomen, then expanding the chest, and finally lifting the upper ribs and clavicle. The exhale is the reverse: first the upper deflates, then the middle, and finally the abdomen pulls in and up, as the Navel Point pulls back toward the spine.

Mantra: Sounds or words that tune or control the mind. Man means mind. Trang is the wave or movement of the mind. Mantra is a wave, a repetition of sound and rhythm that directs or controls the mind. When you recite a mantra you have impact: through the meridian points in the mouth, through its meaning, through its pattern of energy, through its rhythm, and through its naad—energetic shape in time. Recited correctly a mantra will activate areas of the nervous system and brain and allow you to shift your state and the perceptual vision or energetic ability associated with it.

Mudra: Mudra means "seal." It usually refers to hand positions used in meditation and exercise practices. These hand positions are used to seal the body's energy flow in a particular pattern. More generally it can refer to other locks, bandhas and meditation practices that seal the flow of energy.

Mulbandh: This literally means "root lock" and Root Lock is commonly used to refer to mulbandh and is routinely used in Kundalini Yoga. It is a body lock used to balance prana and apana at the Navel Point. This releases reserve energy which is used to arouse the kundalini. It is a contraction of the lower pelvis—the navel point, the sex organs, and the rectum. It coordinates, stimulates, and balances the energies in the lower triangle (first three chakras). This bandh is frequently applied at the end of an exercise or kriya to crystallize its effects. Root Lock is a smooth motion that consists of three parts: First contract the anal sphincter. Feel the muscles lift upward and inward. Once these muscles tighten and move, contract the area around the sex organ. This is experienced as a slight lift and inward rotation of the pubic bone, similar to stopping the flow of urine or Kegel exercises. Then contract the lower abdominal muscles and the Navel Point toward the spine. These three actions are applied together in a smooth, rapid, flowing, motion.

Naad: The inner sound that is subtle and all-present. It is the direct expression of the Absolute. Meditated upon, it pulls the consciousness toward expansion.

Naam: The manifested identity of the essence. The word derives from Naa-ay-ma, which means "that which is not, now is born." A Naam gives identity, form, and expression to that which was only essence. It is also referred to as the Word.

Nadi: Channels or pathways of subtle energy. It is said that there are over 72,000 primary nadis throughout the body.

Navel Point: The sensitive area of the body just below the umbilicus that accumulates and stores life force energy, also known in Eastern martial art traditions as the hara. It is the reserve energy from this area that initiates the flow of the kundalini energy from the base of the spine. If the navel area is strong, your vital force and health are also strong.

Negative Mind: One of the three Functional Minds. It is the fastest and acts to defend you. It asks, "How can this harm me? How can this limit or stop me?" It is also the power to just say no, stop something, or reject a direction of action.

Neutral Mind: The most refined and often the least developed of the three Functional Minds. It judges and assesses. It witnesses and gives you clarity. It holds the power of intuition and the ability to see your purpose and destiny. It is the gateway for awareness.

Nitnem: Literally "repeated every day"; referring to the daily Sikh prayers.

Panj Shabd: Panj means five: *Saa Taa Naa Maa*, that is S, T, N, M, A. It is the "atomic" or naad form of the mantra Sat Nam. It is used to increase intuition, balance the hemispheres of the brain, and to create a destiny for someone when there was none.

Pauri (pauree): Literally "step" or "ladder." Refers to a particular poetic form used in the Siri Guru Granth Sahib.

Pavan Guru: Literally, the "breath of the guru." It is the transformative wisdom that is embedded in the patterns of breath, especially those patterns generated in the expression of naad, in sound or mantra.

Pingala: One of the three major channels (nadis) for subtle energy in the body. It is associated with the flow of breath through the right nostril and represents the qualities of the sun—energy, heat, action, and projective power. It is associated with the functions of the sympathetic nervous system but is not identical to it or derived from it.

Positive Mind: One of the three Functional Minds. It elaborates, magnifies, extends, and assists. It asks, "How can this help me? How can I use this? What is the positive side of this?"

Prabhupati: The third stage of spiritual discipline, when one's own will is aligned to the Will of God.

Prakirti: The creation, the creativity, the matter that has been created by the Creator. Earth is Prakirti.

Prana: The universal life force that gives motion. It is the breath in air. It is the subtle breath of the purusha as it vibrates with a psychophysical energy or presence. Prana regulates the modes and moods of the mind.

Pranayam: Regulated breathing patterns or exercises.

Pratyahar: One of the eight limbs of yoga, it is the synchronization of the thoughts with the Infinite. To quote Yogi Bhajan; "Pratyahar is the control of the mind through the withdrawal of the senses. The joy in your life, which you really want to enjoy, is within you. There is nothing more precise than you within you. The day you find the you within you, your mind will be yours. In pratyahar we bring everything to zero (shuniya), as pranayam brings everything to Infinity."

Purkha: The Creator

Raj Yog: The Royal Path of Yoga.

Saa Taa Naa Maa: See Panj Shabd

Sadhana: A spiritual discipline; the early morning practice of yoga, meditation, and other spiritual exercises.

Sadhu: A disciplined spiritual person.

Sahasrara: The Crown or 10th Gate; the 1000-petaled lotus which opens upon the awakening of the Kundalini.

Sat: Existence; what is; the subtle essence of Infinity itself; often translated as Truth.

Sat Nam: The essence or seed embodied in form; the identity of truth. When used as a greeting it means "I greet and salute that reality and truth which is your soul." It is called the Bij Mantra—the seed for all that comes.

Segmented Breath: A pranayam that divides the breath into clear segmented parts in specific ratios.

Seva: Selfless service.

Shabd: Sound, especially subtle sound or sound imbued with consciousness. It is a property or emanation of consciousness itself. If you meditate on shabd it awakens your awareness.

Shabd Guru: These are sounds spoken by the Gurus; the vibration of the Infinite Being which transforms your consciousness; the sounds and words captured by the Gurus in the writings which comprise the Siri Guru Granth Sahib.

Shakti: Universal creative energy; one's self-projection; feminine aspect of God; God's power in manifestation; woman. The creative power and principle of existence itself. Without it nothing can manifest or bloom.

Shuniya: A state of the mind and consciousness where the ego is brought to zero or complete stillness. There a power exists. It is the fundamental power of a Kundalini Yoga teacher. When you become shuniya then the One will carry you. You do not grasp or act. With folded hands you "are not." It is then that Nature acts for you.

Shushmana: One of the three major channels (nadis) for subtle energy in the body. It is associated with the central channel of the spine and is the place of neutrality through which the Kundalini travels when awakened. When mantra is vibrated from this place it has the power of soul and consciousness.

Siddhis: Occult powers.

Sikh: Sikh means a seeker of truth, and refers to one who follows the Sikh religion.

Skh Dharma: A living experience of values as taught in the Siri Guru Granth Sahib and exemplified by the 10 Sikh Gurus.

Sikh Gurus: In the Sikh tradition there were 10 living Gurus and one Guru, the Shabd Guru—the Word that guided and flowed through each of them. This succession of 10 Gurus revealed the Sikh path over a 200-year period. They were:

1st Sikh Guru: Guru Nanak	6th Sikh Guru: Guru Hargobind
2nd Sikh Guru: Guru Angad	7th Sikh Guru: Guru Har Rai
3rd Sikh Guru: Guru Amar Das	8th Sikh Guru: Guru Har Krishan
4th Sikh Guru: Guru Ram Das	9th Sikh Guru: Guru Teg Bahadur
5th Sikh Guru: Guru Arjan	10th Sikh Guru: Guru Gobind Singh

The 10th Sikh Guru, Guru Gobind Singh, passed the Guruship to the Siri Guru Granth Sahib, which embodies the writings, teachings, and sound current of the Gurus.

Simran: A deep meditative process in which the naam of the Infinite is remembered and dwelled in without conscious effort.

Siri Guru Granth Sahib: Sacred compilation of the words of the Sikh Gurus as well as of Hindu, Muslim, Sufi, and other saints. It captures the expression of consciousness and truth derived when in a state of divine union with God. It is written in naad and embodies the transformative power and structure of consciousness in its most spiritual and powerful clarity. It is a source of many mantras.

Sitali Pranayam: A cooling breath done through the curled tongue.

Sohang (or Sohung): "I am God, God is me."

Spiritual Name or Destiny Name: A name that describes the spiritual destiny a person should strive for in life.

Sukhmani: Peace Lagoon; a prayer written by Guru Arjan, the Song of Peace.

Tattvas: A category of cosmic existence; a stage of reality or being; a "thatness" of differentiated qualities. In total there are 36 tattvas. Each wave of differentiation has its own rules and structure. The final five tattvas are called the gross elements and have the phasic qualities and relationships of ether, air, fire, water, and earth.

Ten Bodies: We are all spiritual beings having a human experience. In order to have this experience the spirit takes on 10 bodies or vehicles. They are the Soul Body, the three Mental Bodies (Negative, Positive, and Neutral Minds), the Physical Body, Pranic Body, Arcline Body, Auric Body, Subtle Body, and Radiant Body. Each body has its own quality, function, and realm of action.

Third Eye Point: The sixth chakra or center of consciousness. It is located at a point on the forehead between the eyebrows. Associated with the functioning of the pituitary gland, it is the command center and integrates the parts of the personality. It gives you insight, intuition, and the understanding of meanings and impacts beyond the surface of things. For this reason it is the focal point in many meditations.

Uddiyana bandh or Diaphragm Lock: Uddiyana bandh or Diaphragm Lock: The name of this lock comes from a Sanskrit word which means "to fly up." In this bandh, the energy of the lower abdomen rises. The uddiyana bandh crosses the mind-body barrier, vertically integrating the emotional qualities and allowing circulation of the pranic energy into the central channel, the sushmuna. Diaphragm Lock is only applied on the exhale. Pull the entire abdominal region, especially the area above the Navel Point, upward and back towards the spine.

Trikuti Mantra: A three-part mantra, e.g. Wahe Guru (*Whaa-hay Guroo*)

Wahe Guru: A mantra of ecstasy and dwelling in God. It is the Infinite teacher of the soul. Also called the Gur Mantra.

Wahe Guru Ji ka Khalsa, Wahe Guru Ji ki Fateh: "My purity belongs to God, all victory belongs to God!"

Yantra: A visual representation of a thought, a concept, or energy which captures the antra, or essence of it symbolically.

Yogi: One who has attained a state of yoga (union) where polarities are mastered and transcended. One who practices the disciplines of yoga and has attained self-mastery.

RESOURCES

The Kundalini Research Institute
Your Source for Kundalini Yoga as Taught by Yogi Bhajan®
Teacher Training, Online Resources, Publishing, and Research
www.kundaliniresearchinstitute.org

The Yogi Bhajan Library of Teachings
Keeping the Legacy Alive! Donate Today!
www.yogibhajan.org

For information regarding international events:
www.3HO.org

To find a teacher in your area or for more information
about becoming a Kundalini Yoga teacher:
www.kundaliniyoga.com

For more information about 3HO music see
www.spirivoyage.com
www.a-healing.com
or your local Kundalini Yoga Studio